CAUTIONARY PILGRIM:
WALKING BACKWARDS WITH BELLOC

This is an entrancing book, in the literal sense of the word. Nick Flint introduces us to his three 'imaginary companions' – though they soon become completely real to the reader – as they journey through Sussex, telling tales, reciting songs, drinking ales and unearthing forgotten mysteries. I'm not a believer, but I found the stories of saints and medieval histories and the secret places of the landscape absolutely gripping. The book has an extraordinary atmosphere; when you finish the walk you will be disappointed it hasn't been longer. So, like me, you will just start again.

John Bird
Satirist and Comedian from television's *Bremner, Bird and Fortune*

A work of engaging wit and style peppered with delightful anecdotes and asides into the history and folklore of Sussex. Nick's love of Sussex – and Sussex ale – shines through, and with the help of amusing illustrations and a cast of delightfully eccentric characters he perfectly captures the atmosphere and enigmatic beauty of the Sussex countryside – Belloc would be proud.

Christopher Winn
Author of the *I Never Knew That...* series of books,
now a television series.

This is a lovely book, soaked in the lore and animated by the Spirit of Belloc's celebrated work 'The Four Men'. Nick Flint and his companions retrace Belloc's steps across Sussex, following his path back to its beginning, but this is no mere 'In the steps of...' travelogue. Rather than simply repeating a journey and commenting on changes between then and now, the formula of many such works, Flint has made a new work, which like Belloc's, teases us with incipient allegories, with suggestions and mysteries as to who he and his companions really are, but all lightened and brightened with quirky,

irreverent, and yet spiritually strengthening humour. A very good read.
Malcolm Guite
Author of *Faith Hope and Poetry,* and *Sounding the Seasons*

Cautionary Pilgrim is the story of Nick Flint's journey through the high-ways and byways of Sussex, in the company of three larger-than-life companions, as they reflect on their 'Sussex patrimony'. Not only is this an affectionate travelogue, punctuated with delightful drawings by the author, it is peppered with unexpected spiritual insights, drawn from the legends of numerous Sussex saints. Nick Flint tells us that the mud through which he trudges 'knows its own and will always gently, lovingly tug us back.' This enjoyable book may well have the same effect.
Nicholas Frayling
Dean Emeritus of Chichester Cathedral

CAUTIONARY PILGRIM
WALKING BACKWARDS WITH BELLOC
BACKWARDS

WRITTEN AND ILLUSTRATED BY

NICK FLINT

COUNTRY BOOKS

Published by Country Books/Ashridge Press
Courtyard Cottage, Little Longstone, Bakewell, Derbyshire DE45 1NN
Tel: 01629 640670
e-mail: dickrichardson@country-books.co.uk
www.countrybooks.biz

ISBN 978-1-906789-93-0

© 2014 Nick Flint

British Library Cataloguing in Publication Data.
A catalogue record for this book is available from the British Library

Printed and bound in England by 4edge Ltd. Tel: 01270 200243

DEDICATION

ACKNOWLEDGEMENTS

Those who walked part of the way with me; Pam and Graham. My imaginary companions are composite characters which reflect aspects of my own personality.

The stories and thoughts which have found their way into this book have their sources in countless conversations with friends over the years and *Cautionary Pilgrim* is a testimony to friends and family who in one way or another have contributed to the process. In particular it was at the suggestion of Charlie Goring that I used the White Lion pub sign in Lewes as the inspiration for the story of Walter.

Thanks are due for practical help in arranging the walk: to Pam Waugh, Anita Greenwood, Graham Whiting, the Chemin Neuf Community at Storrington, Mother Cynthia and the sisters of the Society of St Margaret at Uckfield. I would also like to thank Gill and Alan Radley, Jim Hanson, Jo Unwin, Gerard from the Belloc Blog, John Dewdney, Annette Lloyd Thomas author of the website johnmadjackfuller.homestead.com, Dick Richardson for relating the radio interview of John Julius Norwich for someone overcome by the weight of Belloc's cloak. I value the wisdom of another 'Four Men': Christopher Winn, John Bird, Malcolm Guite and Dean Nicholas Frayling.

My wife Sarah has supported me in numerous practical ways and shown great patience as this project has unfolded.

I have often felt that the late Peggy O'Byrne has been cheering me on and record my sadness that she did not live to read the book, but my gratitude for our shared love of the county which is home to both of us. This is not a book about Belloc. I have not read extensively enough of his prolific output to offer that nor do I feel the need to place him in a mould of my own making. Nor is this a book on Sussex although it could not be set anywhere else. It is specifically not a book of Sussex saints yet I'm as surprised as anyone how often they seem to pop up in these pages.

My father had ended his journey and mine was about to begin. This journey had been passed to me as a gift in the form of a much thumbed volume just as his own father some sixty years before had given the very same book to him.

Who can possibly say how many paths cross and how often, sometimes without obvious consequence, other times with significant effect at the time or interpreted as such much later on. Just a few days after the death of my great grandfather in a Sussex Workhouse, another man, twenty five miles away, was at the start of his own special pilgrimage. It was late October 1902, that man was Hilaire Belloc and the walk he was about to undertake is immortalized in the extraordinary book – an early edition of which I was now holding in my hand; my grandfather's copy. I had long dreamed of making this journey and now the time had come.

I was standing, not as I'd once imagined I might be on the anniversary of the start of the actual walk, on the spot where it began,

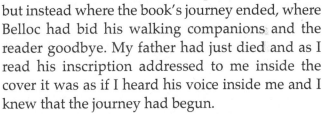

but instead where the book's journey ended, where Belloc had bid his walking companions and the reader goodbye. My father had just died and as I read his inscription addressed to me inside the cover it was as if I heard his voice inside me and I knew that the journey had begun.

It was in that precise moment that I became self consciously aware that I was being observed. For how long this someone else had been there I don't know, but as I met his eyes there was a smile and I immediately relaxed and hailed him as a fellow walker. 'You are reading Belloc.' He observed, and I nodded, thinking he must have good eyesight for a man of his age or perhaps some other gift? He looked to me to be approaching seventy years of age, upright and wiry and to be attired in some ecclesiastical garb modified for practical outdoor purposes. My inquisitiveness as to what this monastic looking figure might be up to was immediately wakened.

His rough blue grey habit owed, with its simple cut more to what might be seen around the fishermen's huts of Hastings than in some grand monastic cloister. A dark heavy wooden cross hung high on his heart. His floppy hat had a seaside air about it too – and I immediately thought of it as his 'Bless me Quick' hat and wouldn't have been altogether surprised to see that legend emblazoned on it.

Standing together on the Downs above Harting we were able to make out through the mists of autumn below, the distinctive copper green spire of Harting Church and clustered around it the few streets and dwellings that comprised the village that, depending on how you choose to look at it, is first or last in Sussex from the Hampshire border.

'From today I am undertaking a walk of my own.' confided the man. 'A pilgrimage in fact' he added. I nodded and smiled to which he asked 'So, perhaps I may join you? After all, 'a man is more himself when he is in the company of others' he quoted, from the book which I had so recently been inwardly digesting, pressing his request with a knowing wiggle of the eyebrows, and that appeared somehow to seal some sort of pact between us. Nor was the company intrusive. His knowledge of Belloc or 'Hilaire' as he preferred to familiarly call him was to prove a bonus.

In repose his lined face bore a weary, even perhaps melancholy air. It was all the more remarkable that whenever he spoke or his eyes met another that his features, especially his eyes seemed animated by some quality that almost appeared to be an inner lustre. I was reminded the first time I noticed it of a flower responding to the sun and basking in the source of the light. His voice at first seemed high pitched in relation to his physique but it carried on the air with a note as clear as that of the oboe above the other instruments of the orchestra.

This may sound silly,' he went on 'but I am heading at least as much towards a time as to a place. In four days it will be the feast of All Saints. I pestered the brothers of my community to let me out for these few days on condition that I return with evidence of the holiness that so many seem sadly to have ceased to believe in. Like the countless forgotten saints it seems even the church may have lost hope in holiness and forgotten where it can be found. My destination is the festival of All Saints.'

'From Sin City to Sanctity?' I quipped, immediately regretting such a flippant, not to say dismissive sounding summary of such a sacred pledge, but 'Pilgrim', the name by which I now thought of him, to my surprise rather than assume any attitude of religious affront laughed heartily out loud. 'Yes – laughter is often the first step, a healthy sense of the absurdity of things. I feel our friend was on that track, and the name his father gave him Hilaire – seems to have set him off and suited him perfectly in that respect.'

I reverently shut my copy of Belloc's *The Four Men*, the inspiration for my walk and put it in my rucksack as we began walking together, to begin with at a slow pace. The first part of our walk with some steep climbing afforded opportunities to stop, appraise each challenging incline as one approached it and to stop again for breath when we had attained it. Otherwise we spent much time alone with our own thoughts only exchanging the occasional remark. I was out of practice as far as any serious walking went and was more than happy to adjust to the pace of an older man.

At the top of one of our climbs I shared my personal conundrum. 'I suppose many have retraced Belloc's journey across Sussex – I'm not sure why, but I decided to walk it backwards'. Laughing at the image that my words no doubt conjured up he immediately twirled round and began himself walking unsteadily backwards, feigning an expression of fear as he made his reply.

'Perhaps you are more likely to bump into the elusive fellow than you would if you were pursuing after him down the years since he last walked this way. Maybe' he added with mock excitement 'There's a chance we may catch him coming in the other direction?' With the insertion of that one word 'we' it seemed as though I had suddenly acquired a companion not just for this stretch but for the county wide walk in its entirety. I began to think that rather than chasing a figure receding into history that Belloc might indeed be nearer than I had first realised. In fact as we talked it emerged we knew of only one other lover of Sussex and devotee of Belloc who had recreated the walk of *The Four Men*. Bob Copper, a Sussex folk singer of international repute had done it in 1950 and with a view to seeing how much the county and especially the roads had changed, repeated the exercise again in the early 1990s, of necessity devising an alternative route in places where the volume of road traffic had increased beyond the imagination of Belloc since 1950 to say nothing of the increase in the first half of the 20th century.

Bob had written an entertaining and informative account of his travels. He had walked predictably enough as Belloc had, from east to west, whereas by doing it 'backwards' I was starting at Harting, almost in Hampshire with Robertsbridge on the border with Kent my destination. The singer had probably been of a similar age to Pilgrim when he last completed it.

We had stopped once more to look down on the peaceful morning scene below. Through a break in the trees we saw framed a perfectly square field below on which sheep appeared to have been placed like pieces in order ready for the start of some Downland giant's board game. From somewhere much nearer however the plaintive bleat of a sheep piercingly if weakly and intermittently, carried on the breeze. Instinctively we looked for the source of the cry and then I saw clearly a sheep that had rolled onto its back and was struggling to get right way up. Immediately I came to the rescue and it was in that moment as I picked the poor animal up that I felt I had grasped the real fabric of the Downs themselves, of which for generations these flocks and their faithful shepherds were surely the rightful inhabitants.

Seeing the tuft of wool left in my hand Pilgrim said 'Put that in your boots. There's nothing like sheep's wool to cushion your feet against blisters, and it's better than holding it in your hand as the shepherds liked to be buried. For them it was a passport to show Saint Peter they had a reason for irregular church attendance.' He had resumed his backward walk as he dispensed this wisdom, but just as he said this, a few yards ahead of us off the path a movement and splash of colour alerted me to the presence of someone sitting in the grass, unseen of course by my apparently careless companion who suddenly seemed in danger of tripping himself or trampling the figure behind him. I gave a cry to look behind him and as I caught up the man got to his feet thinking he would have to allow the backwards walker past. The man we had disturbed was holding a small sketch pad on which a pencil drawing could be seen.

'I'm sorry' my new friend said to the stranger although I have to admit that he didn't look excessively contrite. 'We were experimenting as regards the virtue of walking backwards.' There was a pause as the man seemed to be taking this information in.

'A good way of not getting lost' replied the other ignoring the narrowly averted injury to himself. 'Every once in a while it is good to look back and memorise the scene behind you. If you take a wrong turn and have to retrace your steps you should be able to almost instantly recognise the way you've been.'

'Very practical' I replied, the novice walker that I was, suitably impressed. I noticed that when he spoke there was the slightest trace of some accent I couldn't quite identify. It suggested to me that he might have travelled a long way with his pad and pencil to make this appointment with us. He was what in times past the Sussex native would have called, without any trace of unfriendliness a 'furriner'. His complexion was dark and his tight curly hair completely white, but whether this foreigner was from Russia, Germany, perhaps the Middle East or even Kent, my ear could not detect with certainty.

'Well I have a visual approach to life' he replied, interrupting my thoughts, brushing himself down and holding up his drawing pad ostentatiously before replacing it in some pocket about his person.

'We are on a pilgrimage' my companion offered by way of explanation. 'My friend is looking for a certain Hilaire Belloc. I am

looking for saints. I fear that my church has stopped believing in holiness so my community let me out on a field trip to see if I could find any.' He made them sound like some rare kind of butterfly.

'And walking backwards helps you spot them?' asked the newcomer, with apparent seriousness.

'Er, could be... perhaps we recognise as

saints those who have tended to go against the grain, choose a different direction, swim against the tide.' As Pilgrim said this he peered around as though some might be nearby in the long grass or caught in the gorse bushes.

In the presence of this third party I became embarrassingly aware that the moment for introductions had come, but I did not know the name of my fellow walker. I was about to come clean when Pilgrim asked him 'you're an artist?'

You could call me a sort of scribbler I suppose and you?'

'I am only a pilgrim, Scribbler and happy to be known simply as that. It is good to be joined by a scribe of the kingdom of Heaven who out of his treasure can bring forth things both old and new.' I congratulated myself that the name I had chosen for Pilgrim was one he felt himself so perfectly close to the mark. There was a pause as they both looked at me. Who was I? I wondered if that was for me to discover; the unspoken question on this journey. Both sensed my hesitation. 'Your journey is a pilgrimage too.' said Pilgrim but the purpose is perhaps not as clear to you yet as mine might seem to be. I think Hilaire would respect your reticence; he would perhaps call you a *cautionary* pilgrim.' I smiled at the reference to the poet's perhaps best known and most enduring if not most profound verses and thanked Pilgrim and Scribbler, but at the same time I knew I was searching for a greater confidence in myself.

As if reading my thoughts Pilgrim said 'Caution is no bad thing in itself of course, and yet taking risks is liberating. The saints I'm looking for have often been judged foolish or silly, but in this part of the country we know 'silly' comes from the old word selig meaning blessed or happy. Silly Sussex has more saints per square mile than any other English county. ' I was not in a position to contradict the assertion, but my respectful silence was immediately broken in an agnostic tone.

'Why should that be?' asked an astonished Scribbler 'What does Sussex have that no other county can boast?' in reply Pilgrim calmly pointed to the ground on which we are walking and gestured towards the soft contours of the Downland landscape spread out green ahead of us and on either side. 'Have either of you been to the Holy Land of Our Lord's birth and ministry?' We shook our heads, almost apologetically, certainly in deference as we sensed we were to be made privy to a matter of deep wisdom and insight.

'The chalk Downs are nothing less than the landscape of the Bible' Pilgrim declared. Long ago Palestine lost, through a changing climate the lush green that clothed its hills. If you took away the grass you would see the line of these gentle hills to be just the same as the Judean desert. When you traverse the chalk desert between Jerusalem and Jericho just as the Good Samaritan did, you are treading the same kind of terrain that forms our weald or and their wilderness – the words even mean the same; the weald means the wild. This land too is holy to God. We are also walking with our Lord on the sea.'

This last comment drew surprised looks from us both. Having our full attention, Pilgrim elucidated.

'Chalk is made of the remains of marine creatures which once formed the inhabitants of a vast sea, although that sea parted centuries before humankind ever arrived to walk over on dry ground there.' I looked in wonder at Scribbler who I saw blowing out his cheeks and miming an underwater swimming action in slow motion. Sheepishly he stopped doing this as he saw us both look at his performance with amazement and recovering himself said, adopting a serious even scholarly tone.

'Is there perhaps a memory of this in the Sussex churches that put fish emblems atop their spires? ' I chuckled at the thought as did Pilgrim but...

'Yes, possibly, and those same churches recall the saints who swam as it were against the current and prevailed in the strength of God if to the confusion of many' added Pilgrim. 'Consider James Hannington who on 29th October this very day as it should happen some one hundred and thirty years ago met his end violently at the orders of a ruthless tyrannical King of Uganda, simply because he brought the message of Jesus to that part of Africa and challenged the authority of such a despot. Hannington, a Sussex lad grew up in privileged circumstances north of Brighton. It is said his last words before being speared to death were ' I have purchased the road to Uganda with my blood ' and it is true that the church has flourished in that part of Africa ever since.'

'Our road by comparison seems a most welcoming and friendly one.' murmured Scribbler thoughtfully. 'HB picked up the skills of a draughtsman in early life.' he went on. 'It stood him in good stead when once with typical romance he tramped, almost penniless, across vast regions of America. He would pay his way by sketching local scenes in exchange for bed and board.' During this speech, he had taken out his own pad and pencil and been intent on producing a drawing which he now showed us. At first glance it looked like one of the sturdy trees that steadfastly guarded the path but as we looked more carefully we detected a human figure seated on an old tree stump.

Not long afterwards we entered the shelter of some trees. Following recent high winds the ground was thickly carpeted with leaves and several large branches lay blown down around us. As our eyes grew accustomed to the dark we perceived a waiting figure sat precisely in the pose Scribbler appeared to have foreseen. She was a slight figure, not young. Her demeanour suggested the essence of purposeful waiting. Sitting very still, her steady gaze put me in mind of an owl and I don't think I would have been perturbed in the least to have seen her flutter up into the branches of the imposing ash tree under which she sat, and resume her gaze from there. Instead she rose to her feet and with a smile walked towards us. No words were spoken immediately. It was if we had come together by appointment. She looked at me enigmatically 'That wool in your boots,' she said 'may prove useful to weave into a tale or two.'

She spoke in an accent that left me with an impression of how I imagine my own Sussex ancestors might have spoken. They say the Sussex accent is long gone and I remember my father telling me that as a young man in the army he had been specifically trained to lose his distinctive rustic drawl, but I sensed there was a time when her accent might have marked her out not just as Sussex, but to the ears of true Sussex folk as from some precise hidden hamlet or village where her family might have lived for generations.

Pilgrim looked at me. 'Is it enough that we are now four?' he said, raising his eyebrows, 'Does it matter that one of the little flock is not a man?' Sometimes one hears a word which must be seized on to and hidden in the heart. I thought this as Pilgrim added mysteriously 'we are all knit together in one communion and fellowship with all the saints in heaven and on earth.'

The three of us gave this lady of the woods an appraising but not unfriendly look which she returned in equal measure 'She looks like someone who *knows*.' commented Scribbler comparing his sketch with the figure seated in front of him.

'Who knows' she echoed mysteriously and again making me think of an owl. At this Pilgrim announced 'We will christen you 'Who Knows'. For a moment I feared he might literally dampen this new friendship by actually splashing her with some of the water from the drinking bottle he produced from the kangaroo pocket in his monastic smock, but he was merely brandishing it before taking a swig. 'I am Pilgrim, this is Scribbler.' I felt in awe of this living embodiment of the spirit of the woods, but found the courage to ask 'Do you know whether you would like to join us on a walk through Sussex?'

'Certainly,' she responded, and immediately divining that perhaps the three of us were not best organised asked 'Now we won't make many miles before dark – have you given thought to where we might lodge tonight? It was true we were weary and the light of day was fading. In answer to our blank looks and mumbles she gave a reassuring smile. We were led downhill by her to where signs of human habitation showed us to have arrived at the outskirts of the village of Duncton. Walking single file along a footpath we emerged

onto the main road opposite the church near where we waited. Before we knew it, a large shining vehicle like Elijah's fiery chariot had stopped, doors were flung open and we were on our way to a nearby cottage. This turn of events came about through the network of church and community in a small village where trusting folk still welcome the stranger and revive them with good food and wine.

Much of the evening was spent planning the next stage of the walk in which we had found ourselves thrown together. We passed the book round, read extracts aloud to one another and pondered many aspects of the tale, each of us identifying with one or another of the companions.

But were there actually four of them?' Who Knows suddenly asked. She appeared to know enough of the subject to see how certainly each of the characters was in all probability a facet of the author's personality, interests and temperament.

Belloc took the name 'Myself, Grizzlebeard was a philosophical man of the world, Sailor and Poet simply described two of Belloc's favourite occupations. 'Perhaps the other three are nothing more than a literary device; mix them together and out could come Grizzlepoet, Mybeardself or Sailbeard!'

'You might as well ask whether the church's doctrine of the Holy Trinity is a mere device.' Pronounced Pilgrim thoughtfully 'I say it is how the story of God is experienced. It may not be coincidence either that the Gospels give us four familiar but distinct faces of holiness to ponder.'

'When HB and G K Chesterton first became friends they were described by George Bernard Shaw as 'the quadruped Chesterbelloc' said Scribbler.

'Belloc was a Christian thinker of course.' I said leaning forward to venture an opinion. 'Maybe his book was subconsciously about his relationship to God in three persons, or perhaps the four men are the four evangelists Matthew, Mark, Luke and John?'

'Belloc and his companions consumed copious amounts of ale on their trek' I observed. 'D'you think if the other three were imaginary, that he drank for them as well?'

'That's certainly as may be.' nodded Pilgrim, ambiguous as to which of our questions he was answering. Then slowly and deliberately stretching his tired neck and arms 'Now a challenging walk lies ahead of us in the coming days and I suggest we retire early to prepare ourselves with as much rest as I am confident we will need. I feel sure that our own walk will reveal its own surprises and mysteries.'

TRISANTONIS

Having followed Pilgrim's advice the morning of October 30th found us ready to resume our walk after an early breakfast. We decided to take a detour through the villages before ascending once more to the Downs. 'The references in the book to pubs show Hilaire's sociable side' said Pilgrim 'and suggest his route never strayed far for long from human habitation.' Having said that we encountered relatively few people on our walk where in 1902 villagers would probably have been working outdoors in close vicinity to their farms, homes and local employment. ' Belloc shows that there is more to Sussex than the Downs' said Who Knows.

'Much more – by a long chalk.' I agreed. 'It isn't just about Our Lord walking nonchalantly on the sea or trailing clouds of glory, but coming down and joining us ordinary folk in the valley, sometimes in the shadow.'

Clearly more than the Biblical three score years and ten with grey wispy hair, Who Knows nevertheless had a girlish if autumnal face and a ready laugh that suited our company well. She always walked steady and upright, her eyes fixed on the horizon. She was able to name the birds we passed. She did not fail to miss and greet by name also the wild flowers at her feet, and so our countryside knowledge was enriched and the harder uphill steps made a little lighter.

We stopped after some time at the village of Sutton. At a crossroads there stood the sign of the White Horse, although the pub sign itself depicted a horse that was weathered and grubby with age, this did not detract from a pub in a fine situation and of good repute. From there we found our way to Bignor and rejoiced that the church door was open to admit us to a sacred space the more beautiful for being uncluttered and pleasingly plain. In due course we came upon the village of Bury.

Standing out among more traditional buildings in the vicinity the village school was the first sight to greet us. It appeared to have been very newly rebuilt, with its distinctive sign which from a distance had first looked to our band of tired and thirsty travellers very much like that of an inn. As we drew closer we saw that it colourfully depicted a ferryman or possibly a woman, plying a small boat.

'In times past a ferry would take travellers across the Arun River at a point further down in the village,' explained Who Knows.

What a fitting symbol of education as being taken and guided on an adventure by our teachers,' suggested Scribbler admiring the workmanship of the sign.

'The adventure of seeing things from another side than our own and taking on board that the journey from death to life is for us all' added Pilgrim 'That is something recognised by all religions'

'The best inns may be places of learning of some sort' I offered 'a place to drink deep from the fountain of knowledge.'

'How very poetic!' said Who Knows with a broad smile.

This profound mood was broken not long after when we had halted outside a house in the village street on which were fixed an unusual collection of carved faces; a horse, a Jack in the Green, a rather smug  looking angel and a mischievous leering character who stuck out his tongue. My companions, it seemed could not resist the temptation to pull faces in imitation of those displayed while I looked the other way pretending not to notice. Eventually as the game appeared to be continuing and their laughter getting loud, I suggested with a polite cough that it was time to move on, fearing that an irate owner of the house might appear at the window at any moment and cause deep embarrassment.

A little further on we came to the churchyard of Saint John's church. 'I had expected a dedication to a saint with more aquatic credentials' said Pilgrim, Saint Peter or Andrew perhaps or....' At this point I interrupted Pilgrim with a cry of recognition for I found myself looking at a familiar name on a gravestone of a man I had once known; a man terribly knowledgeable about cricket and something of an expert among many other things on the practicalities of looking after goats. Here he rested in peace, close to the wall of the church and within a walk of the river. To see him there brought back grateful memories of his kindness to me. We left him with a quiet prayer.

'From here we walk down the river for a while towards Amberley.' Who Knows assured us. Pilgrim looked doubtful 'Like Saint Peter? 'he queried mischievously. 'There is a bridge further down.'suggested Scribbler helpfully as we stood looking at our reflections in the slow moving water. 'It is many years since the ferryman used to take people across.'

'This is our first river crossing of four.' I remarked, feeling as though there was some mystic significance, some rite of passage. 'Perhaps we should mark it as such?'

'Well I know what HB would do, find hospitality in a pub and refreshment in Sussex ale' said Scribbler and taking him at his word we increased the length of our strides and within twenty minutes were under the roof of the Bridge Inn raising jugs of the finest Sussex brew, where Pilgrim reminded us in 1902 Belloc and his crew had sheltered from the rain. The weather had smiled on us thus far and The Bridge held one more surprise for the chef turned out to be none other than George – an old friend from times past. No Sussex

man he, but from far flung Greece and now as then proclaiming passionately something that we four well understood as had indeed Belloc, a desire to be at home. And secure in the knowledge that we were doing something, albeit symbolically about reclaiming our Sussex patrimony we set off on our way with, as we headed east, the first of the four great Sussex rivers now behind us.

'Physical landscapes are defined by the rivers that run through them. The sheer power of tons of water is one of the greatest forces on the planet' said Pilgrim, throwing out his arms as if to embrace the scenery around us. 'Carving valleys, borders and nation, the names of rivers, the Nile, Amazon, Thames, Jordan, powerfully evoke countless stories that have created a cultural identity, as well as quite literally bringing life to a region.'

'Arun, Adur, Ouse, Cuckmere' As I recited this litany the voices of the others one by one, joined my own, so that the name of the furthest river from where we now stood became a shout from four voices.

'Time like an ever rolling stream' is symbolized by any river.' Said Pilgrim, continuing his theme 'We talk of time passing as water that has flowed under the bridge. But the river is also a symbol of eternity, because it is the constant factor in the changing landscape. No matter how ancient its water always runs fresh and there is always the mystery of when and where it begins and where it ends.'

There was little to be added to Pilgrim's customary eloquence on this subject. We had reached a fork in the conversational path.

'Who was the *first* saint of Sussex?' asked Scribbler who had been pondering the extraordinary story of James Hannington and his sacrifice, and inspired by such courage found himself wondering, as indeed we all did, what or who in turn had inspired him. We were at the top of the Downs having found our way up from Amberley and were sharing lunchtime rations before resuming the walk east.

'Well the first Sussex saint wasn't a Sussex man at all' said Who Knows, since the others including me still seemed to be chewing the question over with our sandwiches.

'I will tell you the story now – as long as we all agree that caution aside, like Canterbury pilgrims of old we should each of us tell our own tale before this walk is over, a story of Sussex told to match our pace, lighten our steps and feed our hearts and minds.'

I had been ruminating on the experience of crossing the Arun and now spoke out loud 'Perhaps we should mark the passing of each of the four rivers of our county likewise with a story.' I suggested.

'Yes – and a visit to a pub, for without these rivers we would have no beer!' said Scribbler.

We all nodded our assent to the idea of keeping our arrangements suitably fluid and with a hearty chuckle Who Knows began: 'Isn't it funny how if you show someone the stars, dragonflies or a sunset as proof for the existence of God they are in raptures of deep faith,'

'Ah! Especially the dragonfly! Such heavenly colours! Such a dance!' cried Scribbler, clapping his hands his eyes aglow.'

Who Knows coughed politely. She had not finished. 'Yes, but if you show the same person a muddy puddle with children playing in it or pigs rolling in it they are not so readily convinced by that there is a God!'

We nodded at this wisdom and encouraged Who Knows to continue.

Well then let me tell a tale of not just once, but twice or more upon a time that happened here in the Kingdom of the South Saxons.

Close to the sea and covered in forest the land of the South Saxons was home to a proud people. The greatest boast of this small kingdom was that it contained an unbelievably huge amount of …MUD. Yes – the South Saxons had the thickest, squishiest, yuckiest, squelchiest, deepest, muddiest mud of any kingdom.' Here Who Knows paused, took a handful of the very substance from near our feet and rolled it in one palm, to make a small clay globe, which she held up and looked at as she continued to speak.

'People said, not that the South Saxon girls were the most beautiful, or even the most gifted or graceful girls to be found anywhere, but that they of all girls had the longest legs, because they were forever sinking their feet into mud from which with a great heave and s t r e t c h they would have to pull their legs out.'

'They may have enjoyed the benefit of a healthy complexion if they put the mud on their faces for restorative purposes.' suggested Scribbler, perhaps from his experience of drawing or painting portraits of those whether revealing their faces in their natural state or cosmetically enhanced.

'King Splat of the South Saxons was the muddiest king in history. There was nothing he and his people liked more than to be stick in the mud, stuck in their ways people, doing what they had always done in the way they had always done it; as it was in the beginning is now and ever shall be. The fame of the muddy kingdom spread far and wide, although few people who had been there returned, and the South Saxons themselves did not often venture far.

In the cold bleak north Bishop Wilfrid wondered about the South Saxons. He had been told that theirs was the only kingdom in these islands that had yet to hear the stories of Jesus and he decided that he must visit them himself. Like them he was a proud man who felt he had to prove himself. He would show the South Saxons, perhaps, that cleanliness was next to godliness.

Having been told that the roads into Sussex, where indeed any existed, were a peril in which man and beast could easily be stuck and fall a prey to bandits, Wilfrid decided to sail by boat to the Sussex coast. As he stepped ashore it was clear to Wilfrid that all was not as it should be in the Kingdom of Mud. He was met by King Splat's once most proud warriors Splodge and Gloop. They were thin and weak with hunger. No rain had fallen for three years, no crops had grown they told him. There was no longer any mud. It is said by some that during this time we lost the music of the mud in the soft sounds of our place names and the names of those simple playful folk whose economy had literally dried up. Under decree of King Splat no longer could be heard the soft sucking soothing of mud like sounds such as sh, or ph but h had to be sounded separately in the South Saxon land and so it has remained to this day.'

'As in Felpham being pronounced Felp Ham and Bosham Bos Ham, …you mean?' Pilgrim asked. Who Knows nodded and continued.

'All Wilfrid could do was fall on his knees in prayer for the desperate plight of this once proud people. Immediately he did so he felt as though tears of compassion had risen to his eyes. In fact the eyelids of his upturned beseeching face were being wetted with the first drops of rain to fall in three long years. The tears of heaven mingled with those of the saint. He opened them to be greeted with the joyous smiles of Splat, of Queen Squelch and the Prince and Princess, Little Ick and Plop. So for Sussex and its people there was a new creation as when God had first made man from the brown earth.'

'And the very first part of the world to be created so Hilaire loved to believe, was this sacred territory of Sussex' said Pilgrim.

'But surely there was a long wait to the harvest?' I asked, a little disappointed at where the story had left off. 'A little rain could not mean instant salvation for the starving'

'Indeed.' replied Who Knows, 'which is why Wilfrid, putting episcopal decorum to one side, at once doffed his mitre and showed the South Saxons how to use it as a net to catch a harvest of fish from the sea. In time they not only made their own nets, but in honour of Wilfrid added tails to the mitre to make it look like a fish.'

'The proper name for those tails by the way, is 'lappets' said Who Knows. It was a pleasing word which we all repeated a number of times until it began to sound like waves meeting the Sussex shore.

'Do you think it was Sussex mud that tamed Wilfrid's pride?' asked Scribbler, mercifully breaking the hypnotic rhythm.

'I feel certain of it.' asserted Pilgrim. 'and some of the citizens of the kingdom of mud, made of the same stuff as Wilfrid, such as James Hannington have had to pass through fire to become useful vessels of God's grace.'

'Our mud is one of our glories.' said Scribbler 'Think of the sight once unique to this county, of Sussex oxen that were used to plough the fields that would have swamped even strong heavy horses and sucked them under. It is said a visitor to Sussex long ago found a hat apparently sitting in the middle of one of our 'roads' he lifted it to find it sat on the head of a man sunk completely in the mud. This man he rescued expressed deep gratitude and hesitating to ask another favour nevertheless wondered whether he might assist him in recovering the horse on which he had been sitting when the mud enveloped them both!'

'The ox is also the symbol of a great saint – Saint Luke' added Pilgrim 'his gospel follows as straight a line as any plough. It directs us while overturning some of our too comfortable notions so that faith can grow.'

'The Sussex ox' concluded Who Knows 'is also a fine example of what can be achieved by patient pulling together in a team.'

At the end of this tale we agreed we were proud to call ourselves citizens of the kingdom of mud no matter if we were dismissed as grubby by others. As we looked at the splashes on our clothes and the clods clinging to our boots Pilgrim remarked that even the great saints are made from the same mud as all of us. Then on behalf of us all he warmly thanked Who Knows for her story and signalling for quiet invited us to continue walking and tell him in due course what we noticed. Meditatively putting one foot to the ground in front of the other it suddenly came to me. At every step there was that slight reluctance of the mud each time to release my boot. The faint sensation of viscosity underfoot gave me a strangely comforting sense of belonging. Pilgrim could see from the smile on my face that I felt it. ' It is as if we belong to this Sussex mud, it knows its own and will always gently, lovingly tug us back.'

'From it we and the saints were made and to it we shall return.' Who Knows' words sounded as if she was rehearsing a solemn church liturgy. We trudged on somewhat soberly for the next mile or so as a result.

The mist accompanied our mood as by now it was thickening and on and off showers of rain had begun falling. We seemed to be adding to it with the visible breaths we were blowing out. A cyclist overtaking us stopped for a friendly and encouraging word assuring us that the great house of Parham lay in the direction he pointed into that mist and that soon we would reach the first descent into Storrington. Looking across and trying to imagine that stately home in all its splendour as drizzle began blowing into my face, I proposed a song to keep up our spirits and almost immediately the rain seemed to desist. Picking up our feet we suddenly seemed to be in good voice as we plucked tune and words from the enervating Sussex air.

Mud, mud,
Good Sussex Mud
We all rejoice in this great Sussex Mud

Sussex Mud is our glory
or else we've no story
Praised be to God for he
chose best Sussex Mud

When God made creation so long, long ago
he was looking for somewhere to start.
He needed a medium in which to begin
for to fashion it all with such art.
And so he alighted on good Sussex soil
where the Garden of Eden would be.
He found what he wanted, the finest of stuff now,
pray, can you guess what that be?

Mud, mud,
Squelchiest mud …

The birds and things hairy, yes – dinosaurs too,
that were found by our friend, Doc Mantell.
Things creeping and fluttering, both tiny and big,
the reindeer and woodlouse as well.
In all of their weirdness and beauty he made things to live here
in land, sky and sea.
And just when you'd think he'd had every idea, came the strangest yet –
that's you and me.

Mud, mud,
Squishiest mud …

When things reach their driest or seem hopeless and flat,
when everything's turning to crud
If you're feeling quite droopy a solution that's gloopy lies at hand
when you reach for the mud
So think of old Wilf, of this kingdom so blessed
and be thankful for great Sussex saints
Then join in glad chorus with right minded folk
and mud's glory will smother complaints –

Mud, mud,
Muddiest mud
We all rejoice in this great Sussex Mud
Sussex Mud is our glory
or else we've no story
Praised be to God for he
chose best Sussex Mud

'That must be the most edifying 'dirty song' I've ever heard!' mused Pilgrim. As we concluded this rousing ditty and began our descent in the direction of Storrington Who Knows said ' I happen to know a priory where I am sure we can stay.'

'I know of it too' said Pilgrim 'and there is more than one connection there to our friend Hilaire. The foundation stone of this holy house of prayer was laid in 1902 the same year in which he undertook the walk. He may have passed this way and seen the workmen at their labours. It was also the year that his new home his adopted country of England officially embraced and welcomed him.

He certainly visited a few years later and gave the prior the gift of a poem, so impressed was he by the hospitality he received from the community here.

It was a threefold welcome. They welcomed him as a fellow Christian, a French compatriot but also as a refugee like them and they showed hospitality to at least one other poet.'

'Who was that?' I asked.

His name was Francis Thompson and he is remembered for a poem he entitled *The Hound of Heaven*. It traces the story of God's loving pursuit of the poet. Thompson's life was blighted by ill health and drug addiction, but he had good friends and a deep sense that God would not let him go. His words have touched countless souls since. The brothers here saw Christ in him and gave him friendly shelter.

Apart from the rule of holy hospitality they knew, from their personal experience what it was like to be on the receiving end of rejection. They were refugees.The Franco Prussian war changed the life of the Belloc family, coinciding with the death of Belloc's father.'

'So perhaps he had a sense of loss somewhere in his soul?' I suggested.

'Of course' said Pilgrim 'and later there was the loss of his young wife and of two of his sons; one in the First World War, another in the Second.'

'But from the beginning he felt embraced by Sussex?' I felt a sudden warm surge of pride that my own homeland like the Kingdom of Heaven had such wide welcoming borders and because it gathered such a variety of folk to itself was destined to be blessed and enriched by Belloc and his like.

As if hearing my very thoughts Pilgrim continued to hold forth on his subject 'Sussex, and especially I think, the East is a welcome place for refugees whether from Paris or London. Just beyond the normal reach of the administrative arm of the English capital protestant free thinkers could hide here in safety, while close to the continent it offered the first friendly port of call for those fleeing across the channel from religious intolerance. So here you find a fertile place for catholic devotion and protestant preaching to grow side by side and maybe over time to fruitfully cross pollinate.'

We came to a door on which was fixed a simple line drawing in bright colours of Jesus washing the feet of his disciples. At the sight of it each of us suddenly became very aware of our tired, blistered and smelly feet. The thought of them thus being soothingly revived would be an enticing one, we all agreed. Pilgrim stepped forward and rang the bell – one that rewarded us with a satisfying clang. We waited but no one came at once. I walked round the side to see if there was another way in but just as I returned unsuccessfully the door was opened and a puzzled young woman took in the strange sight I'm sure we must have presented. In her hand she held a wall-paper brush, rather than soap and a towel. We exchanged private glances that seemed to envisage Our Lord using such a brush to teach his followers some profoundly spiritual lesson. After a moment's hesitation on her part she beamed a welcoming smile. Pilgrim made himself our spokesman. He lifted his Bless Me Quick hat, and spoke under her searching look. 'Forgive me, I kept you waiting' she smiled, revealing a French accent. 'We are putting up wallpaper' she explained 'I came from France six weeks ago' she continued, opening the door wide to admit us 'My name is Marie.' Puzzled perhaps by the names with which we introduced ourselves, she listened politely as I ventured 'It is a Frenchman you could say, who brought us here actually, and he knew the brothers here.'

'Really? The last of the brothers left only a few weeks ago then we arrived to begin repairing the house.'

'We' turned out to be Chemin Neuf, a fledgling Roman Catholic community in comparison to the Norbertines the previous tenants at Our Lady of England Priory. Since as Pilgrim informed us Saint Norbert had founded his order in the 12th century.

'It is simple here, but there are many rooms where you can stay,' Marie added, indicating one of the bathrooms 'but don't use that one – there is a problem with [she struggled to find the word] 'ah – the plumbery.'

Twenty or so minutes later, having thrown off muddy boots we were sat round a plain refectory table in an otherwise almost empty hall. Tea, as refreshing as any foot washing, had been made and a plate was piled high with biscuits. The small community gathered round the table proved to be an international and ecumenical one. Oliver, a Lutheran from Bremen, Natalia from Poland, Ula from Belgium explained a little about Chemin Neuf's aims. Then they returned to work and we were left to explore the building at our leisure. Who Knows remarked on the smell 'you can tell the place has been empty a while' Pilgrim wrinkled his nose 'A stale institutional smell' he agreed. There was an air not so much of neglect, the place in fact felt distinctly loved, I mused aloud but that through sheer size in the face of dwindling vocations to the traditional monastic life it had proved too much I supposed, for a handful of monks to maintain.

'Not monks, properly speaking; there were actually the White Canons' Pilgrim corrected my observation from his area of knowledge and expertise. 'They arrived in 1882 thrown out of their abbey in France by an anticlerical government. This place was not built for another twenty years. 'In 1902' I shot back, surprising even myself with the speed of my mathematical agility, or remembering Pilgrim's earlier comment. Meanwhile two older married couples arrived to complete the community around a supper of rice and delicious stew. Afterwards we were ushered into what in 1908 had been the Prior's study and shown where over the fireplace had hung the three paintings that had inspired Belloc's lines following his visit and entitled 'On Courtesy'. The classical scenes depicted had been by Italian masters: the Annunciation, the Visitation of Mary to Elizabeth, and the Mystic Nativity. The blank empty wall of course conveyed nothing of what had so moved Belloc to heartfelt verse, but despite the absence of such works of art, the warmth of welcome reflected most of all the image of service, roughly drawn that had first greeted our arrival at Our Lady of England's Priory. We felt privileged to be among the very first visitors at the start of a new chapter of service for this historic build-ing, and in following our ancient path to have chanced on a 'new way'.

As the evening drew to a close we gathered in the darkened chapel for a period of silent adoration of the reserved sacrament, a simple ceremony during which we became aware in the stillness of how the great, once glorious building creaked and echoed. Across the vast emptiness of the institutional space through stale heavy smells, arose a clear light note, a fresh fragrance of welcome carried on the breeze of the Holy Spirit.

In this autumn season it felt like a green shoot growing through the ruins of the old, like a dry brown shell splitting to reveal the shiny new conker within.

Having slept on and off through a night punctuated by the ringing of bells for various arcane hours of prayer I rejoined the others in chapel for a service of prayer and song in greeting of the new day the last in the month of October. A theme of our prayer was the mutual pain felt by denominations that feel themselves divided. Before we left, Scribbler chose to offer payment for our hospitality 'in the same spirit' he said as 'HB' had offered his poem. He produced drawings in his own style of the masterpieces that had once graced the walls here and placed them in the blank spaces where Lippi's Annunciation, Aberinelli's Visitation and Botticelli's Mystic Nativity had once hung.

SORE

From Storrington we set off early in bright sunshine. Turning off the main road we soon left the houses behind and were climbing to where we could enjoy a fine view of the sandstone ridge a stretch of which runs along this part of the county. From that vantage point we carried on across the heathland and in and out of small wooded areas richly carpeted with freshly fallen leaves, some acorns and chestnuts among them, which made it hard to pick out the path through the trees.

Pilgrim led the way at a confident brisk pace, pausing only briefly to draw in large draughts of the fresh morning air fragranced with an almost ecclesiastical whiff of wood smoke, before ploughing on. Who Knows seemed similarly driven as though this day held some particular imperative, and I was conscious of the extra effort of keeping up which it took me with only short stops.

Finally we came to rest when I raised my eyes to see Who Knows and Pilgrim in animated conversation. I looked behind for Scribbler and saw he wasn't in sight. Propelled forward by this realisation I quickly caught up with the others to alert them to Scribbler's disappearance. The other two exchanged frustrated looks and it was decided there and then that we had no choice but to slowly begin retracing our steps, especially as I could not be sure when exactly Scribbler had dropped back 'I hope the poor fellow has not met with some mishap.' said Pilgrim, a note of concern creeping into his voice. We had not gone far when to our relief we saw our friend sitting perfectly relaxed, on a stile intent on drawing, pad in hand and with a faraway look of concentration in his dreamy eyes. It became evident he had completely lost track of time. 'We were worried you'd fallen or taken a wrong turning in the woods!' said Who Knows raising her voice and pointing an admonishing finger.

When he failed to respond she raised her tone another register and merely let fly a non verbal sound of explosive frustration

Scribbler literally *drew himself* up to his full height, indignant for a moment that the need to stop and stare had not been recognised, it seemed to him, by his fellow walkers as they hastened on. He silently made an eloquent gesture towards the sky and we could not but admire the way the light fell through the canopy of branches, he gestured wordlessly towards the nuanced reds, gold, yellows and oranges of the leaves around us and when he had our full attention, he spoke.

'The deeply implanted habit of ignoring Nature is an attitude I have set myself against. When our attention is suddenly called to it how can we not politely pause? How do you think God feels when we never look him in the eye, but rush on past? He said meeting the gaze of each of us in turn.' Before we had a chance to reply he went on.

'An artist must be possessed by Nature. He must identify himself with Nature's rhythm. The effort will prepare him to express himself or herself' he added, nodding towards Who Knows. 'As one of my teachers used to say – where nature ends great art picks up.' This little speech was delivered in a tone and manner of such unself-conscious sparkling joy, that even Who Knows bowed her head with humble assent and after embracing her, bright eyed and smiling Scribbler walked on with us. We had crossed Sullington Common and Washington Common and passed through a quarry where the extraction of clay reminded us again of the timeless worth of our Sussex mud, and now we emerged at the side of a busy main road, new since the time of Belloc. At a nearby roundabout an underpass was provided by which we could enter the village of Washington by the road Belloc had followed and into a pub, on which he heaped perhaps the highest praise he ever had for any hostelry.

The Frankland Arms was empty of customers at the hour we arrived at this inn for which Belloc reserves the highest possible praise and we engaged the landlady in friendly conversation and informed her of the quest that had brought us through her door. She immediately nodded her understanding, for she assured us countless others were still making this very pilgrimage. She told us of one in particular, an elderly man of failing memory who nevertheless had been able to recite for her Belloc's *West Sussex Drinking Song*. We did not offer a rendition of that particularly eloquent hymn to the glories of ale, but drank up and resumed our journey. Bidding farewell Who Knows suddenly said 'May your God go with you.' I could not at first think where I had heard that particularly resonant form of farewell.

'Now imagine if you will, a sight which would have gladdened Belloc's Roman Catholic heart, but might at the same time have caused him to wonder whether he had imbibed too much ale.' Who Knows teased us, as we walked down the steps leading out of the pub. 'What sight would that be?' asked Pilgrim, intrigued. 'Coming round the next corner a litter carried by four cardinals and sat on it in all his pontifical pomp, his holiness the Pope!' Seeing us stunned into puzzled silence Who Knows continued. 'A few years ago an irreverent comedian by the name of Dave Allen sometimes visited these parts to film surreal sketches. One of his entertaining  subjects was in the unlikely spectacle of the Pope being conveyed about in a litter.' Then the memory dawned on me that Who Knows' words as she left the pub had been Dave Allen's catchphrase.

However no such strange manifestations of Rome's might were vouchsafed us as we passed through Washington and set off on a path taking us right past Chanctonbury Ring. The site of an ancient hill fort and subsequently of Roman temples, but for the last two hundred years or more clothed with a grove of trees the ring has attached to it many legends and associations.

'Here Cuthman, the shepherd saint passed by when those temples were relatively recent ruins,' said Who Knows. 'He had heard the Gospel on his mother's knee and she had heard it from Wilfrid himself. When she became elderly and infirm Cuthman put her in a cart and pushed her eastwards, in the same direction in which we are travelling. After enduring the derision and laughter of the locals, when his cart collapsed at the town to which we are headed he took this as a sign from heaven and built the first church the people of Steyning had seen.'

'Perhaps whether he had travelled by papal litter, he would have received a little more respect and fewer laughs than Dave Allen did.' I ventured to suggest.

We were making good time and so decided to take a detour to admire Chanctonbury at closer quarters before walking down into Steyning. We met no-one on the path, but sitting close to the Ring with a picnic lunch spread out before him with almost liturgical precision we could make out an old man in a purple shirt and wind blown white hair who raised his cup in salute to us as we passed. Our route crossed the so called 'Monarch's Way', reputedly the route taken by King Charles the Second as he fled after defeat at the Battle of Worcester and sought to escape across the channel into exile. We pondered the large number of pubs associated with the mix of history and mythology surrounding the broken king's flight, calculating that indeed if he had hidden in the vicinity of each  and every 'Royal Oak', his flight would have taken some years and that if he had taken drink at every such inn he would indeed have lived up to the title of Merry Monarch.

We had reached the corner of a field. A muddy and waterlogged path lay beyond it and to get there we had to climb a stile. Landing heavily the other side we were splashed liberally with mud, momentarily forgetting our esteem for its holy properties, which at other times we were happy to praise in vocal singing. Further into the woods we noted how the water in little streams lay as still as sheet glass.

Spending some time in Steyning allowed us to satisfy fully our need for liquid refreshment. Here we found the Chequers where The Four Men had met the objectionably rich and miserable Mr Deusipsenotavit. Here too outside the church was a statue of Cuthman and right alongside the Star Inn a gushing stream led us to follow the Adur River towards Ashurst the route we took as we listened to Scribbler.

'My story' he began 'concerns a priory but one much, much older than the one where we recently stayed.'

'Imagine lifting off the top of a monastery at the height of the Middle Ages.' Said Pilgrim 'What I am sure would strike you would be the ceaseless movement. Don't imagine the monastic life as one of idle contemplation. The peaceful grassed over ruins of today once hummed with purposeful rhythm; processions moving through the church and cloisters and like a hive, producing a graceful glowing fragrance that glued together the communities of inside and out, the living and the departed. The loss of a pulsing powerhouse of prayer to a town or village should not be underestimated.'

I was fascinated by the image of the hive, and was reminded of an ancient Sussex superstition.

'I know that Belloc continued the Sussex custom of 'telling the bees'. I said 'Those who kept bee hives as he did, would visit them whenever there was a birth or a death or other news.'

'Just as I suppose that folk in the past would take such news to the priory where it could be taken up into the unceasing prayers of the place,' replied Pilgrim

'Is it coincidence that 'telling the bees' sounds exactly like 'telling the beads' in other words praying with a rosary?' Scribbler wondered out loud.

'It's a thought, isn't it, that a simple mishearing could over time have led to a false etymology which then developed into a ritual!' chuckled Who Knows. 'But I'm impatient to hear Scribbler's story.'

At this, Scribbler put his pad in his coat pocket and perching his pencil behind one ear, began:

'In the early years following the Norman Conquest, Count William de Warrene and his wife Gundrada pledged themselves to undertake a pilgrimage. Who knows what stain of guilt from the field of Hastings or in other conflicts the conqueror's henchman wished to make amends for before he met his maker? His exploits and his loyalty to his Lord William had made him an exceedingly rich man. It has been calculated that by the standards of the 11th Century he was richer in real terms than Bill Gates in our day.

This powerful man yet recognised one far greater. He and his wife, the lady Gundrada resolved to make a journey to Rome to seek the blessing of the Pope to build a great church. But the path to Rome was closed to them and the pilgrimage cut short at Burgundy. The renowned Abbey of Cluny was there and showed them its famed hospitality. The priory which he returned to England to see built was inspired by and modelled on the piety, vision and dedication he had witnessed at Cluny. That old story is well known but mine is from the time a little later when I'm told for the first and so far the only time an Englishman was Pope, and a great granddaughter of Gundrada ruled much of Sussex and Surrey from her castle in Lewes. The recently consecrated priory church surpassed its much smaller original and following its completion new tasks beckoned beyond the cloister.

Prior Matthew was the most generous and gentle hearted of men, but it would be a mistake to see this as softness. For all his kind and sympathetic words and gestures there was a look of steel in those grey eyes that spoke of his self discipline and Gospel toughness. Under his wise leadership the priory flourished; prayer was deepened, the poor served, the Gospel held holy. It was Father Matthew's particular care and delight to raise up young monks graced with skills of drawing and painting. Bands of them were sent out to bring colour to the parishes, decorating the plain drab walls of the local churches with fresh and lively depictions of the gospel scenes and the joys of holiness. These paintings had to be of the highest standard. Brothers Scribbleonius and Stenric were postulants apprenticed to an experienced band working at the time on the church of St Michael.

Good Father Matthew always took a keen and close personal interest in how the work was going. He became sadly aware that the work of one of the postulants was tending to his own glory, not the glory of God. This Brother Stenric frequently disregarded instructions and indeed ridiculed the simplicity of the work of some of the brothers more knowledgeable and gifted than he was. The humble prior called the young man in and gently but firmly sought to persuade him that his spirit was not in the work. Stenric was therefore assigned to other more fitting tasks within the priory, specifically for a time at the rere dorter. After some grumbling in the matter it came to pass that both postulants brother Stenric and brother Scribbleonius realised that their vocation lay not in the cloister and in due course with the blessing of the Prior Matthew they returned to their previous occupation.

Sometime after these things the priory received an embassy from the Lord Archbishop. The Archbishop's men came without warning to appraise the priory. They were cold and distant, for it was said certain charges were laid against the prior with regard to the treasures of the priory. It was alleged that these items the prior had appropriated to his own use, indeed in some instances sold and on the proceeds adopted a lofty way of life that made the order a scandal and disgrace.

Assuming throughout this underserved ordeal, the deportment of a sacrificial lamb and refusing to defend himself from such charges the prior was removed from office. When his brothers who knew well that he was innocent, protested at this injustice the prior asked them to be still from their defence. He not only surrendered his leadership of the community, but submitted himself to a humiliating public penance. He ended his days as Brother Matthew – the swineherd in the community he had once led.

At the same time, the paintings in the church of Saint Michael's were defaced and whitewashed over by some unknown hand.

Those who in later years visited the Brother Swineherd in those later years, testified to his serenity and in the pig sty to a palpable atmosphere as of a chapel, the presence of holiness. A simple window looked out and up onto the Downs. That beautiful scene could only and always be glimpsed through the rough hewn cross which formed the window frame.

Brother Scribbleonius after he left the order prospered in worldly trade and many years later wished to endow the priory that had taught him so much of life.

In that village church in the faithful brothers of the priory's best band of preachers in paint devoted a chapel to a depiction of the story of the rich man and Lazarus. It was said that the poor man in the painting resembled somewhat the beloved former prior. He was however not shown as a beggar, but a noble figure of stature of the fullness of Christ, the image of a man fully alive and possessed by God, perfect in proportion and fitness, but perfected by the sufferings portrayed as a divine victim commending his spirit to his loving father, then being comforted by Abraham.'

'Your story, Scribbler, puts me in mind again of Francis Thompson.' said Pilgrim 'Lazarus had his wounds licked by the dogs. It is unclear whether he should have felt violated or comforted by such attention from fellow outcasts.'

'That woman in the Gospels who begged Jesus to heal her daughter, called the dogs to witness her plea and softened the Lord's heart.' responded Scribbler.

'And Thompson personified the Lord's pursuit into that of a hunting hound, but discovered one more likely to smother with affection than sink in tearing angry teeth' said Who Knows.

'I think' I said 'that after leaving the order Brother Scribbleonius must have married and raised a family and that you are of his kin and have inherited his artistic skills.'

'Thank you!' beamed Scribbler 'The story has been passed down through the artists in my family since time out of mind and is certainly one that tells of the power of pictures.' I marvelled, as one whose eyes had been opened in a gallery of wondrous new sights. 'They say the camera never lies but the painted likeness of Lazarus tells the truth about Prior Matthew that has endured centuries beyond the cowardly lies that were heaped on him.'

'It is my experience,' laughed Scribbler 'that innocent pictures –

 even some of my scribbles – have been able to terrify by truth telling far beyond anything I set out intending to draw out. Two of my cartoons were actually su-pressed by church dignitaries who I suppose because of their own insecurities thought I was criticising them. In doing so I felt they judged themselves – I am greatly relieved to say that isn't my job.'

'Now as for art that takes the breath away, you will find at Saint Peter's church in this locality a remarkable treasure created to commemorate a rather more worldly but nonetheless great prior in his own way. Having somehow slipped through Protestant iconoclastic clutches it found its way to Cowfold. Perhaps even a century after his death Prior Nelond had family in the village who wished to honour his memory, it is otherwise a mystery as to why his impressive brass likeness came to rest here of all places. Perhaps old Bishop Sherborne of Chichester had a hand in it, rescuing such things as these just as the new broom of the Reformation swept in to take him with it.'

Whatever the story, here we too came to rest weary as we were from the day's travel.

Finding the door providentially unlocked we wondered if the invocation of Saint Peter at *Cowfold* had any connection to the flowers *cowslips* being known in folklore as Saint Peter's keys, which it was imagined he had once carelessly dropped somewhere in Sussex.

As we stood in the aisle of the darkened church, Pilgrim silently flitted here and there lighting such candles as he could find until we were enveloped in a warm evensong glow. We offered prayers of thanksgiving for the road that had brought us this far. We thought of Saint Matthew 'whose Gospel of love wears a human face.' Said Pilgrim 'and puts wings on the feet of those who like the tax collector are called to a light that outshines all their gold.'

'Tomorrow' said Who Knows 'we have a long journey ahead. We will find our way into East Sussex through Lower Beeding and Pease Pottage then going south again.'

'But how come,' I said 'that we have come north to Lower Beeding when Upper Beeding is further south?'

'Many who are first shall be last.' Said Pilgrim and holy Sussex is itself a parable attesting to that promise. We climb hills that are called Downs, the lower place name is above the upper as we also find at Upper Dicker and Lower Dicker, and we are walking backwards to discover the true order of things.'

'Is that a Magnifisfact?' asked Who Knows cheekily, in reference to Our Lady's evening canticle that we had just recited among our prayers. In response Pilgrim had composed his own hymn, inspired he said, by Scribbler's story.

Then in the stillness we raised our voices in song, to an ancient tune from the nearby locality of Kingsfold for which it was named.

As evening creeps upon the world
Sky darkens, all is still
We join our voices with the one
whose song accepts your will
She could have been a Sussex maid;
such know how 'up' comes 'down',
that those whom life brings low yet may
rise to a throne and crown.

As darkness falls and lights grow dim
Yet vision may increase.
An inner light that shines within
the source of hope and peace
may find the faithful hearted soul –
– the true and lively saint
stands out more vivid as the flame
flickers on sacred paint.

Old faces gazing from the wall
once whitewashed, now revealed
tell how real holiness endures
God's promises are sealed.
Then let us raise our voices up
with Mary as she sings
in company with Sussex saints,
giving our praises wings.

We awoke the next morning to more singing as Pilgrim's solo voice was raised in the canticle 'Benedicite' the song of the three in the fiery furnace who found themselves delivered by a mysterious fourth figure who appeared in the flames. 'O all ye works of the Lord bless ye the Lord; praise him and magnify him for ever' rose to the roof and as we left the church our breath could be seen in the cold air. Today the only fire among the grey trees was in the warmth of red, orange and yellow leaves, so to warm ourselves further we improvised some off the cuff praises.

'O all ye Pilgrims of the Lord bless ye the Lord; both bold and cautious praise him and magnify him for ever

O all ye scribblers bless ye the Lord; Michelangelo and Heath Robinson praise him and magnify him for ever

O all ye shepherds bless ye the Lord; silly woolly flocks praise him and magnify him for ever

O all ye pubs and publicans bless ye the Lord; watering holes of the righteous praise him and magnify him for ever

O all ye Sussex saints bless ye the Lord; obscurely dedicated churches praise him and magnify him for ever

O Sussex East and West bless ye the Lord; from Kent to Hampshire praise him and magnify him for ever

O Hilaire Belloc bless ye the Lord; In the name of Grizzlebeard, the Sailor and the Poet praise him and magnify him for ever.'

MIDWYND

Emerging at the start of the next day's walk we greeted the new month and the great winter feast of All Saints. Pilgrim, walking out of the church, stretched his arms in a sun salutation, although the sunlight was masked by mist. Scribbler immediately began doodling, and Who Knows was gazing intently at the activity of some birds in the distance. As we set forth we were approaching this point from a different direction of course than had Belloc and his fellow travellers. We also arrived at an immediately recognisable landmark from the book, the Crabtree Inn, somewhat earlier in the day than did Grizzlebeard the Sailor, the Poet and Myself ….. Even drinkers such as they may have baulked at taking alcoholic refreshment before eight in the morning. Outside the inn we stopped and Pilgrim reminded us of the occasion of the visit of the Four Men and a rendition of a particularly raucous song.

'I wonder if there are songs which like some rivers have gone underground these days' I said ' I mean of course that people are listening not to live music so much as having it piped into their shops, their cars and pushed unmediated into their ears…'

'You are not the first to voice concerns of a similar nature' conceded Scribbler. We turned to Who Knows who stepping out of her own reverie observed that it has always been possible to carry a tune around in one's head, so perhaps we need not be so alarmed. She went on;

'Some of those peoples the superior minded may like to refer to as 'primitive' have long believed in 'Song lines' – the idea that music lives in certain locations, or along certain routes, rising and falling with the landscape calling to those who take the time to listen as did John and Lucy and Ralph…and Bob.'

'John, Lucy and… who are they?' I asked.

'John and Lucy were the Broadwoods; uncle and niece who both set down the songs of our native county which, never having been written down were in danger of becoming lost. Ralph Vaughan Williams was one of our well known English composers of music. He helped and encouraged Lucy after her uncle the Reverend John Broadwood had passed on the task to her. Our friend Bob Copper, of whom I believe you've heard was until only recently patriarch of a family who preserve and hand on the same tradition, having the advantage of living at a time when the technology was such as to make possible permanent recordings of the sounds of Sussex. It may also be no coincidence that music of a rather different kind was much later recorded by pop bands at a secluded recording studio almost on Lucy's doorstep.' She inclined her ear towards the ground cupping it with one hand.

'But for the folk singers isn't it the live singing, the oral tradition that remains essential?' I asked.

She nodded, still cupping her ear and with a most intent and mysterious expression on her face, so that we all stilled ourselves perhaps expecting to hear too whatever it was that might be calling.

'What can you hear?' asked Pilgrim finally.

'A little way from here is a church where John and Lucy lie buried.' she replied. 'Morris dancers still make merry there on May Day every year. I once heard Bob sing while standing under the porch of the very same church and although that was long ago, I think I hear something similar again now.'

At which remark a solemn but peaceful and happy stillness settled on us. We skirted the great town known to Belloc as Horse Ham 'Hilaire, no lover of big towns, actually though used to bribe the station staff to announce that trains had arrived in Horse Ham – the old pronunciation, rather than Hor *sham*.' Pilgrim told us.

'I know for a fact that the parson at the very church of which Who Knows speaks joins every year in a jolly chorus of that much loved May day ditty *Hal an Tow* and issues a yearly amnesty that allows the local dragon to take a pew should he wish, within its hallowed walls, knowing that St George will indulge him with a friendly welcome, for he is a friend beloved of Muslim and Christian and glad to sheathe his sword and speak peaceably.' I said and when they looked blankly at me I set off singing lustily as we went into the woods:

Robin Hood and Little John have both gone to the fair-o
And we've been to the jolly green wood to see what they do there-o.
And for to chase-o to chase the buck and doe

Hal-an-tow
Jolly Rumbalow
We were up
Long before the day-o
To welcome in the summer
To welcome in the May-o
for summer is a comin' in and winters gone away-o

Where are the Spaniards that make a great a boast-o?
They shall eat the goose feather and we shall eat the roast-o
In merry England the land where ere we go.

It was a simple tune to pick up and on the second chorus they joined in with me and sang with gusto.

Hal-an-tow
Jolly Rumbalow
We were up
Long before the day-o
To welcome in the summer
To welcome in the May-o
for summer is a comin' in and winters gone away-o

As for our good knight St George, St George he is a Knight-o
Of all the knights in Christendom St George he is the right-o
In merry England the land where ere we go.

Hal-an-tow
Jolly Rumbalow
We were up
Long before the day-o
To welcome in the summer
To welcome in the May-o
for summer is a comin' in and winters gone away-o

God bless Aunt Mary Moses with all her power and might-o
Bring peace in England bring peace by day and night-o
In merry England for now and evermore.

Hal-an-tow
Jolly Rumbalow
We were up
Long before the day-o
To welcome in the summer
To welcome in the May-o
for summer is a comin' in and winters gone away-o

As the last strains died away we congratulated ourselves on our rendition of this anthem, unseasonal and at times incomprehensible though it might seem to the casual listener, rambler or honest dog walker who might overhear us in those woods.  Scribbler, though was scratching his chin in deep thought and in case we hadn't noticed finally asked 'Who is Aunt Mary Moses? 'With an expression that looked like 'I'd hoped you weren't going to ask that.' Pilgrim opened his mouth but nothing immediately came out. Coming to the rescue, I suggested 'Maybe it is something corrupted over repeated mis-hearings – could easily be 'Our Mary' rather than Aunt Mary...like Our Lady.' I sensed Scribbler and Pilgrim were waiting for an explanation of Moses' seemingly random appearance, but then Who Knows came in turn to *my* rescue.

'Robin and Little John were off to see the 'Fair O' weren't they which could sound like Moses' arch enemy Pharaoh?' She met our sceptical looks with a convincing follow up. 'Illiterate Sussex folk famously used a double plural which famously confused talk of fairies by referring to fairiesies. The listener could easily hear 'Pharisees' and make a connection with the Jewish partisans referred to in the Bible.'

With this the balance of plausibility seemed satisfied on all fronts, and we returned to paying due attention to the direction in which we were going.

Following a mossy fingerpost that pointed the way out of the woods we found ourselves at the bottom of a large sloping field. Climbing slowly to the top of it we were rewarded with a panoramic view of the Downs behind us and in the far right corner against that glorious backdrop the spire of Parkminster Monastery which Pilgrim pointed out as yet another foundation of French monks fleeing their own country in the 1800s. I marvelled at the impact of events just across the channel on the landscape of our county.

'We have heard more than one story of monks on the move and I know that Saint Ignatius Loyola said members of his Jesuit order should have always one foot firmly on the ground and the other raised to begin a journey.'

But turning our conversation back again to folk traditions Who Knows suggested further 'or – why not – to begin a dance! 'The parson of whom you speak seems to realise that the church is in reality the original folk movement.' I said 'It is such clergy as these who a hundred years and more ago were in the forefront of affirming and reviving folk song and Morris dancing for instance.

'Sometimes the liturgy of the church is choreographed like dance,' agreed Pilgrim.

'Old Harry' was a dancer and singer, well remembered in these parts and known for keeping the tradition alive' I said 'and I can picture him in exactly that suspended pose.'

'May the footprints of our saints be of those who keep us in the excitement and suspense of possibilities!' said Pilgrim performing a jig of his own.

'As for Pilgrim's talk of a dragon it is said that such beasts have indeed inhabited these woods to which we shall soon come ' Who Knows went on, looking askance at Pilgrim's eccentric choreography. 'The village of Colgate's most frequently quoted claim to fame is as the home of the last English dragon seen here in the early 1600s. It inhabited the forest and was as these creatures are always reported, a source of trouble to man and livestock.'

The writer William Cobbett took to the saddle in the early 1800s to explore and write about as much of England as he could, described this stretch between here and Crawley, a small market town in his time, as 'the worst six miles in the whole of England.'

'You mean, because of the fearsome dragon?' I asked accompanying the question with a comic roar and suitable mime for effect.

No that was long before his time' chuckled Who Knows, for her part miming her fear.

'Despite such dark tales as these and Cobbett's malediction the forest is named for a saint and the river Arun which rises in these woods, Belloc himself highly exalted as did our medieval ancestors who honoured Our Lady at a chapel in these woods. Perhaps there is a sense in which these opposites must always live close side by side in order to be seen for what they are?' I asked Pilgrim.

His answer was 'Light and dark need each other. The saints are like cat's eyes in the road. They show us the direction which we are to follow, they reflect the light, the potential for holiness that is in every one of us, but in so doing they stand exposed and vulnerable in a dangerous and sometimes dark place.'

Like Belloc all those years before us we raised a jug or two at the Black Swan, a pub which after a brief period honouring Horsham brewer James King had reverted to the title by which Belloc and friends would have known it. Heading west from Pease Pottage as they had been in 1902 a few years later the 'Four Men' might have met on the road coming the other way from the village of Colgate an itinerant preacher in the shape of a certain Brother Edward. Like Belloc, he was one who would walk great distances and on one occasion left Colgate where he had been for some time assisting the vicar Father William at Saint Saviour's Church. Having outstayed his welcome as far as the commanding officer at a nearby army camp was concerned he was on his way to a parish in the Midlands. He

 had been ministering in difficult circumstances to men who were about to embark for the Western front, many of course never to return.

Today Pease Pottage is a name most usually identified with the eponymous motorway services, a concept which in 1902 would have eluded the grasp

even of the at times prescient Belloc, understandably so when perhaps the number of cars on the roads might have been numbered in scores rather than hundreds.

'I wonder how many motor vehicles the four men saw on their journey across Sussex – there can only surely have been only a handful in the whole of the county at that time?' I suggested.

'One of the earliest ones actually belonged to Rudyard Kipling. He might have been out and about in it when Sailpoet was strolling through Brightling, not far from Kipling's new home at Batemans.' Who Knows assured us.

'While one of the poems in Cautionary Tales seems to extol the car' she continued 'anecdotes suggest that in later years especially he became intolerant of modern noise not least that of traffic outside his door.'

'It invaded the peace and quiet he so prized and needed for thought and writing I expect.' suggested Scribbler. 'After all, that must have been part of his delight in discovering a rural retreat.'

'Wasn't Belloc a rival of Kipling?' Who Knows asked.

'I believe they were reputed not to get on' agreed Pilgrim. 'If so it might have been old fashioned professional jealousy, or perhaps Kipling like others mistrusted, Hilaire's devotion to the Roman Catholic faith as 'un English.'

'Or perhaps' I suggested 'there was no one particular reason, but it was **Just So**'! Pilgrim looked over the top of his spectacles pityingly at me while the others groaned unapologetically at the pun.

So we hastened on through Staplefield towards the next village of Balcombe. Belloc might once have relished lively debate with an alleged heretic who was once vicar here but the road beckoned, and such was not our purpose.

We felt at first welcomed like the prodigal son, or so it seemed to us, to Balcombe with yellow ribbons, but a large flashing display warning motorists of the presence of pedestrians on the main road suggested all was not well here. Even the prodigal son of scripture did not return to a household without tensions. We met a lady walking her dog and asked her what this all meant.

Somewhat wearily she explained that the drama playing out here was unlike anything she had ever experienced here in the village of her birth a period of some 70 years. The fields were lush with dew and the views took in the autumn colours. All could not have appeared more peaceful and inviting to the casual observer passing through as we were. Just out of sight beyond the trees she assured us the ground had been torn up and residents subjected to the constant loud moans and groans of machinery and deep tremors from below ground. It was all in the cause of locating and extracting valuable gas for fuel, a process known as fracking and performed by a group known by a name that had the misfortune to sound like some mythical and enraged monster rather than a corporate body of no doubt perfectly rational businessmen in smart suits simply doing their jobs. My mind went back to Colgate and the dragon – was this story being played out in another Sussex village such a new one I asked the others.

'Such legends speak of the community placating and appeasing with wealth situations which seem to threaten our own sense of power and control. They buy them off like some kind of insurance policy, but the threat instead of going away becomes more demanding until the situation is resolved by the intervention of a Saint George or similar hero.' pointed out Pilgrim.

'In the history of our nation and because of natural resources particularly fuel, huge progress has made. We became industrialized on a grand scale but now the structures and systems built on such success demand greater and greater energy to sustain.' said Who Knows.

'The roar of fire and belching clouds of smoke were indeed at the time of the last dragon a more familiar sound in the woods of Sussex than bird song and babbling brooks for here was our first industry located. The woods provided the raw material for huge furnaces to be fed and ore extracted locally was smelted into iron goods, not least the first weapons of mass destruction – cannons which were produced on a huge scale here beginning in the 1500s,' Pilgrim said with a heavy sigh.

We walked on, continuing to discuss how, typical of many of the communities in our county of Sussex the material benefits of living in a village like Balcombe are not to be denied. Life in Sussex compared to a living in less prosperous and comfortable parts of the world might seem almost a fairy tale 'happy ever after' existence. As to what price the modern dragon or 'Giant Fracking' has had to be paid to ensure such prosperity continues, the question raised by recent events in this village we realised, will continue to be debated.

Some miles south out of Balcombe we followed a track through a farm which boasted a large and impressive herd of cattle, whose sedentary demeanour I had always been taught to interpret as a warning of impending rain. The public footpath took us through a field behind a smaller second farm. On a slight rise four sheep regarded the four of us with what might have passed for friendly amusement. Scribbler noticed at once that one of the four had a  white face, the others black, and said it felt that we three men and one woman were looking at sheep versions of ourselves. The sheep were also familiar in the sense that they came up to us without fear. Perhaps they thought they recognised us too.

Ignoring a seductive path which snaked off in the wrong direction we beat a way upwards through brambles and were rewarded with the sight of a beckoning finger post which confirmed our direction. A few miles further on a silvery white shimmering through the trees to our left turned out to be the southernmost edge of the reservoir at Ardingly.

At one of the farms along Plummerden Lane Scribbler suddenly stopped and brought us to a halt. There stood at the side of the road a bare lightning blasted oak.

'Look closely, 'he said 'what do you see?' to begin with we all gave different answers – a dragon, a giant foot, tin of paint, a tree, fairly obviously. It took us time to agree but agree we finally did with

Scribbler that the face of Belloc – an angry looking Belloc it seemed at that, to look out across the road. It seemed a somewhat pagan medium for the orthodox Roman Catholic to adopt should he wish to make himself known yet the more we looked the more like him it appeared to be.

'Belloc's nickname was Old Thunder' said Who Knows, darkly 'He was born during a storm at a time when the clouds of war were gathering over France.'

'He could be devastatingly belligerent,' added Pilgrim feeling the rough surface of the tree, 'but at other times revealed a soft hearted side.'

'So his *bark* was worse than his bite?!' I suggested.

'Or he should have shared the nickname Boanerges – Sons of Thunder, with two of Jesus' disciples.' Said Pilgrim, speaking again.

The sight of a pond opposite and a few ducks swimming contentedly on it presented an entirely more peaceful scene that immediately revived Who Knows' happier spirits 'In Sussex dialect they are called paddlequacks.' She told us, as we delighted in their comic antics and Scribbler got out his pad and pencil to capture the moment.

Also along that same road we saw a species more recently introduced to Sussex – llamas, who pressed their faces up against a fence to watch us go by. Soon a sign proclaimed that we had left West Sussex behind us, as if to confirm the change in scenery we almost immediately saw our first oast house normally associated with Kent and the far east of our county.

A little further on it seemed suddenly for a moment as if we had indeed stepped back a hundred and eleven years in time on our walk to 1902. A railway bridge spanned the road ahead and as we looked a train pulled by a steam engine crossed it, sending up puffs of white smoke and steam.

'Of course, the Bluebell line runs across this way. 'I suddenly remembered out loud. We carried on under the bridge as the sound of the train receded until only the cloud could be seen silently drifting upward.

To our left Sliders Lane led surprisingly to Heavens Farm. Scribbler said it made him feel we were walking across a great map made out like a snakes and ladders board.

'I had always thought that sliders were going the other way… and that Heaven involved the effort of climbing.' He remarked.

'Then' Pilgrim said 'you are forgetting the moral of Grizzlebeard's song at the Crabtree Inn when Belloc railed against the heresy of Pelagius.'

As he spoke I pictured in my mind's eye the vision of that angry Belloc thundering and flashing angrily.

'Pelagius and his heresy being who and what exactly?' I prodded him.

'Thinking we can get into heaven by our own goodness. Why, what a club of the insufferably self-satisfied heaven would be then! Almost the whole point of the church and the Bible is that God loves failures! Pelagius himself was a Celtic monk, probably from the British Isles whose name became synonymous with religious smugness.'

'In that song I notice HB *thanking* God for 'howling heretics' said a puzzled Scribbler.

Pilgrim thought for a moment 'It could mean he wants to hear them howl in pain or that he is actually grateful to them for their errors or 'howlers' if you like, which show others what to avoid. Personally I prefer the latter interpretation. It is often the challenging opposite view the antithesis that has challenged the church to keep journeying on in the search for truth rather than sitting on the laurels of its theological treatises. Some I fear work from a false etymology linking heresy and hearsay, in a desire to catch people out.

Without the so called pagans' hunger, without their sense of such a close connection with trees, hills sky rivers and <u>mud</u> what common ground would Wilfrid have ever found with them? We've seen that he learned as much from the South Saxons as they did from him. If heresy means taking the risk to dare think differently, then thank God for it, for that in my book is how we got our theology in the first place.'

'I recall hearing of a rather precocious curate who took his vicar aside after the Sunday sermon and said 'Father, I think you preached heresy today' said Who Knows 'Yes ' admitted his vicar, 'and next

Sunday I shall preach the opposite heresy to balance it out.'

Pilgrim chuckled and nodded enthusiastically 'Quite right. I think Belloc held some firm opinions but was broad minded enough to have been able to see heresy as like walking and therefore just as necessary an exercise. He once described the physical act of walking as an astonishing balancing trick that involves avoiding one potentially fatal error of judgement after another to reach one's goal.'

'Which in his case was probably the next pub!' I added triumphant at bringing the discussion down to earth.

Pilgrim added' What would have made him angry I'm sure, was that honest searchers after truth, like the vicar of Staplefield can be bullied and forced to resign.'

At Fletching my appeal to Belloc's drinking nature was readily heeded by my companions and we drank deep of the local ale before turning our attention to the church across the way. 'Here' said Who Knows before we went in 'can be found the tomb of  one of our greatest historians. Pushing the door gently open the four of us stepped inside, anxious to discover of whom Who Knows spoke – who of such stature could be laid to rest in such a humble church? A suitable Latin inscription indicated this as the resting place of Gibbon, the 18th century chronicler of the decline and fall of the Empire of Rome. Enclosing his final resting place had been done with the intention of making it a feature, but we noticed had the unfortunate effect of lending itself to becoming a convenient broom cupboard. Among other things, a bucket sized (empty as far as one could tell) tub of mayonnaise had been unceremoniously placed at the foot of the great man. Or perhaps it was some form of Roman pagan offering that had survived into the Christian era. We retreated in confusion to resume our walk eastwards. Rain, of which I thought the cows had warned, had held off, but we had covered many miles and notwithstanding our refreshment we were feeling weary.

Glancing southward we had a distant view of Isfield, a village that formed from early times close to the ford where a Roman road crossed the river Ouse or to give it its ancient name Midwynd. This was the river whose mouth had welcomed the white canons from France, Pilgrim reminded us.

'Not far from the the site is an inn at the sign of the Laughing Fish' pointed out Who Knows.'…a fact that would have delighted Grizzlesail.

As the miles to Uckfield began to be marked off on one sign after another, Pilgrim cried out as if to encourage us 'At least we aren't obliged to make our way there through deep snow!'

The remark seemed strange. It was if

Scribbler had deliberately drawn a large cartoon question mark to hang in the air and as if pointing to such a feature I supplied the question pilgrim had provoked by his weather observation.

'What do you mean?'

Scribbler cleared his throat with a suitably polite accompanying gesture and adopted an 'I'm glad you happened to ask me that' tone of voice.

'I was referring to a very well known Christmas hymn that was penned hereabouts by one of England's most prolific writers and translators of hymns' then with a pause for dramatic effect he added '…Neale!' and at once Pilgrim solemnly and knowingly with a wink to me and Who Knows, genuflected.

'No, no!' Scribbler turning round and seeing this gesture, regarded him with exasperation. 'I didn't say kneel, I meant John Mason Neale.'

As the words left his lips he recognised at once from the look on Pilgrim's face that he had deliberately misunderstood for pure fun. 'of course you would know about John Mason Neale,' he said.

'It is a story that deserves to be as renowned as that one hymn of his among countless others.' At which he began at first to hum the tune and then to sing the words of 'Good King Wenceslas, which we all knew so well. When we got to the part between king and page Pilgrim took the first in a deep bass while Who Knows sang the part of the page. Then we paused to allow Scribbler to tell us about Neale.

'Although his ministry was based in East Grinstead a significant part of his legacy is to be found in the town we are approaching. He was in the forefront of restoring the religious life in the form of orders such as the sisters of The Society of Saint Margaret...'

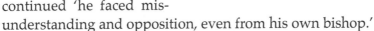

'... another saint who faced a dragon..' interrupted a voice, that sounded like Who Knows.

'In doing so' Scribbler continued 'he faced misunderstanding and opposition, even from his own bishop.'

'In his master's steps he trod.' I sang and continued with a laugh ' I knew a parish priest who after a fall of snow liked to be the first to visit the church. He would walk backwards to the entrance to give the mysterious impression that someone had left the church before anyone had arrived.

'On at least one occasion' Pilgrim continued 'Neale and some of his sisters faced physical assault at the hands of an angry and ignorant mob, while one of them indeed lost her life ministering to the victims of contagious sickness.'

Scribbler concluded. 'While he was by temperament a scholar, and a prodigious one at that, he came to rejoice in having mud slung, metaphorically and perhaps literally at him and experienced the furnace of mis-understanding and criticism from a church that has always seemed to struggle to recognise the prophets in her midst. His Society of Sisters was called on to see, to serve and to love in the midst of poverty, ignorance and illness. Their work continues today in many countries and places of need and it all started here in Sussex. So, Pilgrim, does Neale qualify among the saints for whom you are searching?

'Why, yes, by virtue of being a silly Sussex man if not by birth then by adoption and confession. Concentrating on stepping aside from every pitfall or predicting every approaching danger would have left him litle time in his short life to simply enjoy the view. After all joy is a mark of the true saint, more than duty for the former is inspired by love rather than fear.'

Then, to the familiar tune so beloved of Father John of East

Grinstead we found some inspired new words to which to march.

Sisters of Saint Margaret;
Strong in prayer and witness
working for God's kingdom yet –
Faith, Hope, Love that's boundless
Brightly shine their godly deeds
Through the mist and darkness
Seeing first, then meeting needs;
Sharing Gospel goodness.

Vision of a holy priest
brought them first together.
Bound in strong community –
Faithful in all weathers
Blessed by God down many years
Blessing many others
Through the good and wise counsel
Of successive Mothers

In the Master's steps they march
Where their calling takes them
helping others in the search
for the pearl, the great gem –
that the Lord has promised those
who love without measure
Pouring richly from his grace
of eternal treasure.

Rough ravines to hallowed heights
always lead us further
through dark valley into light
promising new birth
Our Good Shepherd of the sheep
knows the way he leads us
waking us from death's dark sleep
to new thrilling purpose.

And as the last line floated away on the breeze we found that we had arrived. At the door of the modest home that was now the convent and mother house of the Society of Saint Margaret, the sisters welcomed us in. Turning to allow the others in before me I looked up and touched Pilgrim

ahead of me, to follow my gaze and see the trail of a single stray firework arcing across the darkening sky. It was at such a distance that nothing could be heard, but it was a harbinger of the approaching bonfire season, observed with particular zeal in this part of Sussex. In these East Sussex towns it is bound up with the folk memory of those who were burned at the stake as heretics less than five centuries ago.

At that moment as I tugged on Pilgrim's sleeve it seemed to me as good as any a symbol of saints who light the way to heaven, transcend the politics of their day and more often than not send themselves up with a little humour. Facing us as we went in was a portrait of Neale, a benign smile on his face.

Pilgrim wished us all a peaceful night's sleep, but reminded us that it was on this night in 1902 that Belloc spoke of being visited in his dreams by the long dead, not that this was something that should be a cause of fear, least of all in such a holy house as this. Sleep, however, did not come easily and when it did there were strange sights indeed beheld by the inner eye.

I was back at the beginning of my walk at Harting with no sign of my other friends. A finger post which said Harting had been graffitied into 'Parting' In the distance a stately house could be seen, and at once I found myself wandering its long corridors, going down into the servants' quarters. A lady sat knitting in an armchair. Her young son walked out of the room and into a waiting spaceship. To begin with it travelled slowly along country lanes stopping and picking up people from rustic looking bus shelters. Then it suddenly shot up into the sky and I was in it looking down at the length of Sussex. The spaceship was piloted by a man of fierce and sad countenance who stood in a heavy black coat at the console. His pockets were filled with French loaves and bottles of Calvados brandy and as a member of the crew took the coat from his shoulders he fell backwards collapsing to the floor with a loud crash under the sheer weight of the coat. Struggling to his feet he spoke gravely to the pilot who was looking down on the county stretched out below him. 'It's Sussex, Captain Belloc,' he said 'but not as we know it.'

And as they watched, the ridge of the Downs like the back of a giant sea creature, writhed and lashed out as if harpooned by the many little houses that were springing up everywhere at speed to obscure the landscape. The boy from below stairs in the grand house began wrestling over the controls with the captain and the flying saucer spun alarmingly faster and dangerously close to the settlements below. I didn't see who finally gained command of the craft, but at length it appeared to fly gracefully over the horizon and out of orbit as peace returned to the county.

After the disturbance of my night visions the morning of All Souls found us gathered early in the peace of the small chapel. French windows behind the altar gave the sense of a light and airy space, even on such a misty autumn morning as this. The woodwork was light and the vestments were white. For one brief moment during the service a beam of sunlight focussed gold on the green of bushes in the garden beyond.

The contrast with the morning service at Storrington was subtle but remarkable. In the dark chapel of the priory church it had felt like a liturgy of longing for the renewal and reunion of the church with the quietly exuberant singing introducing an unmistakable note of hope.

Perhaps because my consciousness has been shaped by a very English catholic faith I responded very differently to a service with a homelier lighter touch in a domestic chapel that not so long ago had been just another room in this house. Added to this was a sense of homecoming specifically to East Sussex and in this Eucharist being able to take part in full communion.

'It was a beautiful service' said Scribbler, but I noticed a trace of sadness in his words and the faraway look that accompanied them.

'What is it?' I asked.

'It seems a pity that only such a small handful are gathered to enjoy this experience.'

Pilgrim smiled sympathetically but knowingly. 'Once, when the man of God was vulnerable and surrounded by his enemies, his servant was surprised at his composure until there came an answer to the prayer 'Open the young man's eyes that he may see that those on our side are more than on theirs'. Immediately the servant saw a heavenly host, huge in number of reinforcements rallied around them. So it is here. This small community is surrounded by angels and saints, the righteous departed and their prayerful associates still on this earth. They may be few in Sussex where it all began but are at the centre of a worldwide society doing great work for good. Those who support the work from afar are united in the cry 'From rough ravines to hallowed heights' and with that we must resume our onward journey with uplifted spirits.

We saw a sign pointing to Lewes 'Where the citizens burn an effigy of the Pope!' announced Pilgrim

'It sounds an ungodly town' I said.

'Far from it' replied Scribbler 'That the people of Lewes are deeply spiritual can be deduced from their attachment to their cathedral, from which like a devout prayer fragrant incense rises and hangs protectively.'

'But...'

I could get no more out before Scribbler burst out laughing at my perplexed expression.

' ...there *is* no Lewes Cathedral, or so you are going to tell me! Yet 'The Cathedral' is how the great brewery that stands along the river is fondly toasted with jars raised and a heavenwards look of pious gratitude to the God who blesses hops, malt and yeast.'

As we set off through the mist we saw encamped a vast army in the fields. Tents stretched as far as the eye could see. The normally small enough to be near invisible multitude of spiders were a presence revealed by the dew on their webs erected on stubble tent poles. Each web magnified in size a hundredfold would indeed have presented the spectacle of a host preparing to join battle.

'Last night, almost unseen and unremarked.' Said Pilgrim, 'we crossed the third of the great rivers that divide our county and I propose to take my turn in marking this just as we agreed with a story of my own...

There are moments when the fog of doubt and isolation clears and one's loyalties and course of action becomes sharply defined.' He began 'Who better than a worker in textiles to pick out and put in perspective the text of our lives? My story concerns such a one: Walter the weaver looked out from the western wall of the town. He lived and worked in a small dwelling close to the fortified western gate. Straight ahead was the hospital of Saint Nicholas. In the distance to the northwest he saw the glint of metal on armour and weapons of a growing army, the colourful pennants of the king's troops fluttering in the wind. In the nearer distance next to the holy well stood the church of Westoute which had so many memories for him. Instinctively he felt the ring on his finger that had been given him he believed by a saint. Walter was not alone in such an estimate of Bishop Richard of Blessed memory. In simplicity and undeserved affliction, Richard had endeared himself to his flock. Walter knew one of the fishermen for whom the bishop had performed the wonder of a miraculous catch of mullet from the bridge over the Ouse. He had his own personal recollection of Richard. How clearly he remembered the day when at the local church he had witnessed the enclosure of Mother Anne the anchoress in her cell'; a solemn ceremony performed by Richard. Afterwards on that occasion Walter had sought and received a blessing at his hand. Then in a typical gesture the bishop had drawn off the ring he was wearing and given it to Walter. It was this ring he now wore, more than 10 years since he had last seen the late bishop pass through the town on his way to Dover and his untimely death. It now seemed to him a sacred relic.

The late father in God had suffered at the hands of King Henry and his rival for the bishopric, Archdeacon Passelewe. Richard was a man of the people who took it all with wondrous grace and humility and finally at the intervention of the Pope, was vindicated. Yet greedy grasping King Henry, ruler since the death of his father King John still clung to power. He was marching west hopeful that allies from across the sea would reach the coast and rendezvous with him, but paused at the great priory of Lewes to seek the intercession of Saint Pancras, avenger of perjurers, which prayers he believed had been powerful on behalf of his great great grandfather, Duke William the Conqueror nearly two centuries before, to say nothing of a former maligned prior of this great house.

Even as the feast day approached and preparations for the great liturgy in celebration of Saint Pancras were in hand at what was the most beautiful, some say, certainly the largest ecclesiastical building ever raised in Sussex. Prior William called the brothers together into the Chapter House. As he had watched the gathering of the two armies, that of the King and that of the barons he foresaw an inevitable slaughter. The younger more able bodied brothers were mustered to be ready to go out onto the field of battle to bring in the wounded, the dead and the dying to receive the ministry of the brother infirmarers, apothecaries and the priests according to circumstances, to be nursed to health or to be given the last rites of holy church. There was to be no difference made between king's men and de Montfort's soldiers.

Meanwhile, after saying his prayers and placing the bishop's ring

 under his rough pillow Walter laid down his head and immediately fell into a slumber in which he dreamed. In the dream he saw a great white sheet held by Bishop Richard and heard him call out 'Where is Walter the weaver?' Walter came forward and was asked to weave a design on the cloth. This he did, not recognising until he had finished that the design he had created was the rampant white lion of the king's

brother in law Simon de Montfort. Waking from the dream he pondered its meaning. It seemed to him that as Richard had asked he should make a banner of the lion and so putting all his other tasks to one side immediately he woke he set to work. When it was finished he set it on a pole and displayed it on the town wall, although aware that this might be considered treason he believed that there were times when loyalty to God's Kingdom might require disobedience to an earthly king, especially one who could show such indifference or unkindness to such a servant of the Lord as Richard had been.

The sight of the lion banner fluttering in the breeze put heart into Simon as he and his knights approached the town wall. It seemed a rallying roar of hope for their cause and spurred on towards it they found a way into the fortified town that secured a victory that day, a victory which forced the king to accept terms that allowed for a parliament with free speech to be set up for the first time in our land.

In time the breaching of the walls would be seen as symbolic of the enjoyment of new freedom and a vindication of Saint Richard in particular and of all his patient and peaceable kind who will always stand up for others but not for themselves.

The memory of the holy was blessed. The monks with their state of the art plumbing knew about the need for a deeper catharis and cleansing. Not only did King Henry make recompense for his misconduct but not long before Simon de Montfort died his campaign for freedom similarly sought to make amends misdeeds of his father, also called Simon, whose misguided wish to purge the church of freethinkers led to the massacre of the Cathars labelled by the church as heretics.

Small of stature, not one in whom one might immediately recognise a figure of authority but truly lionhearted, Walter lived to a good age, was among the crowds who finally celebrated Richard's canonisation and the translation of his holy relics, then spent his final days kindly ministered to at the hospital of Saint Nicholas where at length he died, his duty done.'

'I happen to know' I added 'that near the site of that hospital many years later a school was built and it came about that a girl from that school was one of a class who took part in an amateur archaeological dig at the site of the hospital. Digging among the ruins she chanced to discover a very old ring...'

Pilgrim smiled his warm approval of my fitting footnote and then added.

'Either walls contain doors to the bigger open spaces or they are designed to confine and stifle, to keep out that of which we are afraid. In time the latter sort will always fall.'

'The walls of the old priory are long gone.' I pointed out 'What rich 'Bill' de Warrene started was finished by a man called 'Gates' actually he was 'Portinari' which is Italian for some kind of entrance or another.'

'But was that really the finish?' asked Pilgrim ' I believe the monks would rejoice and see that their work continues, for they did not construct such walls to shut the world out, but in their prayers brought the needs of the created order into their workplace, a prayer powerhouse as hot as any furnace. As I see it the making of their land into a park, an open space where, yes – children can play and learn is a very fitting memorial to their work and indeed I say, a kind of continuation of it, opening the cloister up and out to enrich society economically educationally and spiritually as monks and even Mother Anne and others like her with a window open on the world have always done. Even the demolition engineer Portinari's twisted design in desecration has turned to good purpose fulfilling the destiny of his name. Such is God's patient work; order out of chaos, life out of death, rejoicing out of ruin.'

'Surely.' agreed Scribbler, for is not man made for enjoyment?'

'To bring joy is a high holy calling' added Pilgrim, his eyes lit up with the most expressive smile, his voice almost singing.' I love that poetic bequest of Hilaire's to the children of Sussex; to each their lot in universal joy!'

'And while ugly walls remain and even as new ones are being built they present a challenge to the artist to transform them into windows, as you will have seen done in the Holy Land today, eh, Pilgrim?'

'Yes, there it has been said that rather than learn the lessons of history they are putting up a new 'wailing wall' and inventing new woes.'

A great painter I knew was a muralist on the grand scale. Hans Feibusch's paintings can be found the length of our county where he found a home and a welcome after fleeing the intolerance of his native Germany.

This story having been told at a leisurely walking pace to give us time to look around and appreciate the Wealden landscape through which we were passing, the end of the tale seemed to signify a new tempo. As we moved on I noticed Pilgrim begin to adopt a determined marching movement as if in time to a military beat, perhaps inspired by the thought of the knights descending on the battle field. I found myself falling in with his rhythm. After some time I began humming in accord with the march, and hearing this low continuous note Scribbler, conducting with his pencil as a baton whistled a melody we all knew. The tune of *Monks Gate* which he gave us seemed highly apposite, as in imagination we saw ourselves setting forth through the open doors of some great priory church.

What came out next, although sung antiphonally like monks in choir conveyed little of the subdued beauty and restraint of gently soaring plain chant such as they would have known. Rather, our Bellocian bellowings would not have been out of place in an old fashioned Sussex beer parlour as we threw verses to and fro.

Me
Those who would Sussex see
Let them walk backwards
Down land and farms and sea
Fields and high weald woods

Come walking County-wide
Take Belloc as a guide
And bound for all saints' tide be Sussex pilgrims

Pilgrim
Those who would Sussex hear
Turn both ears backwards
Monks chant musical prayer
Coppers and Broadwoods
Come walking County-wide

Scribbler
Those who would Sussex smell
Lift noses upwards

Sea air, tar, river tide
Scent of smoky woods
Come walking County-wide

Who Knows
Those who would Sussex know
Let them walk backwards
Reverse of high and low
Folks like Saint Richard

Come walking County-wide
Take Belloc as a guide
And bound for all saints' tide be Sussex pilgrims

When our song was finished Pilgrim offered a reflection on the place of the lion in the story. 'Of the Gospel writers, it has been adopted as the symbol of Saint Mark. The lion is usually shown as a winged beast.'

'A beast of pray?' I suggested, but ignoring such a painful pun and quite rightly too, Pilgrim pressed his point further 'Mark's is the Gospel of immediacy, the shortest and most direct in tone and language. He invites us to be bold and take risks. We can otherwise be so cautious and calculating as to lose our sense of adventure.' This felt as though it was directed to me in particular. 'The roar of the lion" he concluded with a roll of the Rs, bids us come quickly to the point.

The sight and smell of autumn smoke rising from a chimney in the distance was welcome and the more so when as we approached it became clear that the chimney belonged to a pub to the door of which

we felt strangely beckoned as if by Belloc himself. Sustenance, we reckoned would be needed for the final stage of the walk, and we were in undisputed agreement as to what form Belloc would have had us refuel.

WANDELMESTROW

With three of the great rivers of Sussex behind us it began to seem as though our journey was drawing to its close and with it the end of our association. At times it had seemed that the many faceted Belloc was somehow close and could pop out at any moment to surprise us. It felt that there were teasing clues regarding Poet, Sailor, Grizzlebeard and Myself carelessly strewn across the landscape.

In Pilgrim's search for saints we had seen many a church and had discovered holiness within and outside their walls. We had supped good Sussex ale in many an inn. We had travelled across downland, through woods and along the leafy lanes of the county even when those paths had been transformed since Belloc's time into a blur of tarmac and traffic. We seemed to have gathered around the four of us a multitude of other fellow travellers from among those whom we met and who populated the stories, songs and memories we had shared. Our footsteps had disturbed the dust of old tales and full flight had been given to our powers of imaginative speculation.

Sensing the ever closer approach of the end of our trek the four of us had perhaps been taking for some time a more deliberately leisurely pace when Scribbler informed us 'A scientific study has recently discovered the fact that on average, city dwellers are walking 10% more quickly than they did a decade ago.'

'So we must be walking considerably quicker than did Hilaire,' said Pilgrim. But he looked puzzled and added 'They can't have based their research on the newsreel films of a hundred years ago when everyone seems to have walked in a very fast jerky motion.'

We were uncertain as to whether or not Pilgrim was joking, nevertheless we deliberately slackened our pace, sensing that the news Scribbler shared was not good for the wellbeing of our planet and its people for were we not forgetting the stature of God in his patient waiting? We were pleased then to allow some usually slow plodding creatures to overtake us at this point.

However, one must walk with a purpose and we had degenerated to an aimless wandering when what must have been an hour or so later, Who Knows, who had been leading the way, came to a sudden and unexpected stop. She turned and raising a hand faced us on the path where it led us into a small copse. 'Does anyone actually know where we are?'

We looked around and at one another and after some muttering amongst ourselves had to admit we appeared to be lost. Scribbler got out his pencil and pad and began writing on it what I took to be calculations. Who Knows appeared to be cupping her ears, while Pilgrim raised his eyes heavenward and for all I know was possibly praying.

Suddenly I had a bright idea 'I have a map' I said and drew the book out of my rucksack, flourishing it aloft. On the flyleaf was Belloc's own hand drawn map of Sussex. Pilgrim stroked his chin thoughtfully, Scribbler laughed and shrugged his shoulders and Who Knows gave me a doubtful look that seemed to challenge me to make any sense at all of Belloc's skills as a cartographer. True enough there were plenty of gaps in the map especially in the north and east of the county that left much – a little too much to the imagination of any would be navigator. The idiosyncratically chosen landmarks were inscribed in Latin which didn't in itself present any huge difficulty. For example, Belloc's home Kings Land was rendered *Terra Regis*. Yes, it was Sussex, but not as we know it. Bounded to the north by suburbia Belloc's 'hic olent' appeared to warn of some unspecified

smell arising from that region. Over the western border was summed up as the haunt of pigs – presumably 'Hampshire Hogs' as the natives of that place are proud to call themselves. On the Kent side horned devils with tails lurked among the hop fields. 'What does caudiferi, mean?' I asked pointing at the word on the map that accompanied the odd looking creatures.

'They are mischievous little devils who taunted St Augustine and his missionaries.' replied Pilgrim. 'Incidentally, at this point we are probably almost exactly just as close to the mother cathedral of the Anglican Communion at Canterbury as we are to the cathedral of Richard at Chichester.'

Interesting that HB a Roman Catholic depicts the Anglican bishop and not the Roman one at Arundel.' said Scribbler pointing to Belloc's representation of a figure with episcopal crook and mitre.

'How did they taunt Augustine?'

That story really belongs to another county but the destinies of Kent and Sussex have often been intertwined.' Said Pilgrim. 'It was a century after the time of Wilfrid. Respect for religious leaders seems to have dwindled to the degree that the people of Kent pinned fish tails to the bottom of his monastic habit – they were punished when their children were born with fish tails' he concluded wrinkling his nose with distaste and shaking his head to signify that he did not condone genetic modification as a form of revenge.'

Who Knows sympathized 'I am an ancestor' she said mysteriously, leaning against a tree behind her and placing her arm around its trunk 'By which I mean, even if I did not have children of my own I care for the generations to come and the ways we are shaping now the world they will inhabit. I pride myself on knowing this county like the back of my hand.' she added, stretching her right palm downwards in front of us so that the veins stood out like venerable tree roots.

She interrupted herself by once again holding a hand to her ear and looking us in the eye to see if we could hear what she did. 'The music of trickling water which I can hear tells me we are not far north of Heathfield. This is the rising of the fast flowing Cuckmere – the last river we must cross.' She said.

Suddenly without quite knowing how it had happened we found ourselves back on what we all knew and felt at once to be the right path. It was as if we had lost someone in a jostling noisy crowd when suddenly above the babble the unmistakable voice of that beloved rising above everything transforms the time and place from one of dread uncertainty to a moment of clarity and the promise of home-coming.

71

'The old name for this place or the way it sounds in Sussex dialect is 'Heffle' Who Knows was saying 'Since the decree of King Edward the Second the town has held by Royal Charter a fair – Heffle Fair, sometimes known as Cuckoo Fair, since it fell in St Richard's tide, when the first call of the cuckoo is heard and Bishop John Langton saw to it in 1315 that the event commemorates that holy and bird loving predecessor of his whom Pilgrim wove for us into his tale.

'*Bird* loving?' I queried.

'Yes' Pilgrim himself interjected by way of explanation. 'He admired them for being at their early morning prayers as dawn broke and sought to emulate them by rising early while it was still dark to prepare himself for prayer.'

'Maybe he was tuning in to and hearing the same ancient song lines that were rediscovered in their times by the Broadwoods and others.' I tentatively suggested.

'Well we've arrived at the wrong season for the Cuckoo' said Scribbler with a slight shiver as a cold sharp breeze sliced through us 'she will be enjoying warmer climes. Anyway, I have been working on a new map' he said, and passed around the pad allowing us to admire his cartographic skills.

'As the guns grew louder the cuckoo fell silent at the outbreak of the First World War' said Who Knows 'the charter was forgotten and only much more recently has Saint Richard's fair been revived.'

'Like his father before him King Edward was making further amends for his own grandfather's poor, one might call it 'cuckoo treatment' of the saint pushing him out and supplanting his rights' said Pilgrim.

A plank bridge brought us out from the shelter of the trees onto a road. We followed its winding course without meeting any traffic. This end of the county seemed quieter with a distinctive sense of stillness.

A little further on Who Knows gave us some insights to ponder 'The further East we go the less pull the gravity of Chichester in ecclesiastical terms and London in the judiciary sphere has sometimes seemed able to fully and effectively exert itself. 'Eccentrics' in the literal sense of those outside the orbit, the circle, become more prolific or at least it is claimed they thrive here more. I forebear to judge to what degree this is a good or bad thing. It may have been exaggerated as for example in the story of the 'petticoat parson' for whose story I have never found any documentary evidence.'

'Who was he? Pilgrim and I chimed in together.

Who Knows laughed at both of us 'That is the point 'He' if indeed the tale has any truth, was a *she*! The story goes that the old Bishop's eyes having become dim he ordained her in mistake for her twin brother, while others maintain that his was a Simeon-like farsightedness – that he was a deliberately conspired with her. The name of the remote village – Amenglade – where they say she ministered two hundred years ago is either a vanished hamlet or a name deliberately constructed to throw scandal mongers off the scent.

I can only vouch for the reasonable possibility of such a thing happening in these remote parts long ago, but must leave it there in the realm of tantalizing conjecture. But it is well known that women disguised as men distinguished themselves in army, navy and medicine at a time when such professions were still the sole preserve of men.'

Scribbler, suppressing his laughter as we bounced along a plank bridge crossing the burgeoning stream, told us 'It is recorded that when HB was about four years old his mother took him to church where he saw Cardinal Manning, the former Archdeacon of Chichester who long before had become a Roman Catholic. Noting the cardinal's robes and finery, young HB asked his mother whether he was a woman or a man!'

Pilgrim listened with interest. 'I cannot pontificate on what Who Knows tells us ' he said with a chuckle, 'but that we are in the region inhabited by those unafraid to be scoffed at for different thinking is well attested in the case of a much lauded character from this part of the county. In early November as we already find ourselves, one sometimes hears the cry 'Vote for Guy Fawkes – the only man to have entered Parliament with honest intentions!' I know of one other who is indeed recalled with the only title he would accept that of *Honest*. John Fuller's honesty as a Member of Parliament was counted madness and folly by some when it led him to cause more than a few fireworks by dismissing the Speaker of the House as 'that insignificant little fellow in a wig!'

So is *he* one of your saints?' I asked, wondering if the saints could ever be rude or deliberately cause offence.

'He was the son of a parson whose brother, young Jack's benefactor rejoiced in the Christian name Rose' Laughed Pilgrim 'Better perhaps to call him a holy fool, though that is a description that fits quite a number of saints. I doubt that it is coincidence that the Christian All Saints tide falls in early November as did the pagan Roman celebration of Hilaria, which licensed all kinds of foolery.' Then he added, not for the first time giving me the impression he had read my thoughts. 'Sometimes saints need to say out loud what others are afraid to say and I think Jack was probably one to speak with a marked lack of caution, which I suspect was what Hilaire admired in him and what made him a role model when he too aspired to be an MP.'

'I have certainly heard him called Mad Jack Fuller' I said.

'Indeed.' Pilgrim answered. 'By reason of his large and rather round build 'hippopotamus' was another nickname he acquired.'

'If he was a hippo then he was certainly one who loved Sussex mud.' Scribbler chipped in. 'And I can understand how if we begin to believe every cautionary tale we can be in thrall to those who maintain their authority with some twist in the tale they like to keep hidden up their sleeves.'

At Dallington we had arrived at a wooded shaw, the slope leading into which was steep so that as we entered it we picked up momentum, almost but not quite enough to launch us all the way up the bank into the field out the other side. Scrambling and breathless it was a wonder none of us fell full length into the mud.

Our talk of Jack Fuller took us back to the age in which while great scientific progress was being made, the rich indulged their follies in buildings worthy of the name with no other purpose than to provide employment for the labouring classes. The Fuller family money came from the local iron industry. Jack supported both science but also such follies with the money his uncle Rose Fuller had bequeathed him. Among them was the so called Sugar Loaf, a conical frippery hastily erected, it is said, to win a wager that the spire of Dallington church could be seen from his window when on returning home he discovered this was not as he had imagined, in fact the case. We were able to see the church for ourselves and it certainly bore favourable comparison with the folly. Within the church we learned that a former 15th century vicar had joined Jack Cade's rebellion, but was pardoned by King Henry VI for his part in it.

'Cade led a number of disaffected Sussex and Kent citizens against the king in 1450. They reached London and caused some mayhem, but returning to Heathfield he was tracked down and killed,' said Who Knows. 'It was felt that the king was not in control of his nobles and had forfeited his authority.'

We pressed on Eastwards and before long found ourselves approaching Brightling Church. As we did so Pilgrim drew our attention to a large pyramid which from the angle we viewed it gave the optical illusion of dwarfing the little church.

'Have we taken a wrong turn and arrived in Egypt?' I laughed staring at the remarkable construction in front of us.

'Not quite' came Pilgrim's quick riposte 'but this last folly, although constructed while he was still alive was to mark Jack's exodus from this world in some style, for it is said he constructed this mausoleum in the churchyard, big enough for him to sit up at a table inside it, and on the table a bottle of claret and glass within reach.'

'That these unusual edifices stand to this day' said Who Knows must be testament to a memorable character in a kind of line of succession from de Montfort who called the first commoners to parliament and to the representation of their shires.'

Pilgrim addressed Who Knows and Scribbler in my hearing. 'Our journey will soon be at an end. We have crossed at its source the last of our rivers, each of whom have a mouth like that of an evangelist, giving forth a message of clear purity to refresh the lands and seasoned with salt. We have left the Cuckmere behind us and we have yet to hear from our friend here the final of our stories.'

'I feel that in some ways we have only scratched the surface of what this county is about.' I said ' but often our small detours and exploring of odd little byways seems to have brought us closest to the spirit of what Belloc I think wants to draw to our attention as making Sussex unique.' I paused to allow him to continue.

Pilgrim invariably spoke in a kindly reassuring tone, his 'sermons' in that sense were all 'homilies' in other words homely accessible illustrations. Now he addressed me directly in an especially gentle sympathetic manner 'The French word for our endeavour is a peregrinage. It puts me in mind of a soaring sharp eyed bird who takes in the landscape at once from a heavenly perspective but can home in on the small local detail. You may if you choose quibble at my doubtful etymology ' he went on turning again to the others 'but perhaps especially for our friend this pere grinage has been a rediscovery of his 'Pere' I mean his natural father, while for all of us such journeys as to be dignified by the term pilgrimage set us on the return path to the heavenly father from whom we all are inclined to stray.'

I thanked Pilgrim for his apt observation and taking up his theme said 'Mine is partly the story of a nobler bird even than the falcon of whom you speak. It concerns an eagle – an imperial bird and it speaks as Gibbon would of the departed greatness of Rome, The stories we have heard beckon us back to a time of mystery and a world very different from our own, but Jack Fuller brings us into the modern scientific age.

My story does not reach back in time anywhere as far as have yours. Indeed, Father Darke a priest whose secret lies at the heart of my tale, died as did Belloc, sixty years ago and only with the discovery of his papers following his death in a nursing home revealed the true story.

A hundred years ago the Reverend Albion Darke was the vicar of the only Anglo Catholic parish in the town where he served – that of

St Martin's. He employed the pulpit of St Martin's to expound such prophetic messages as the social needs of the poor, equality for women, and perhaps most controversial of all as time went on, pacifism. He involved himself in the arts and especially amateur theatre,  forged links with other Christian denominations, and as far as recreation went was something of a local historian and archaeologist. In 1912 he made the astonishing discovery of a remarkable artefact of the Roman occupation of Britain. Excavated from the clay banks of the Cuckmere that ran across the bottom of his vicarage garden, it was the emblem of an eagle from a standard to which centuries ago would have rallied the legion.

Darke wrote and submitted a monograph on his findings but it went largely ignored. Not only were other supposedly more dramatic archaeological discoveries rewriting the history books at precisely the same time, but his political views had made him enemies among the worthies of the town who considered that nothing truly of note would be likely to come from that quarter. Darke bore this lack of recognition with humility and patience being a scholar for who fresh discoveries broadened mind and spirit.

I have said that Albion Darke was a committed pacifist, but he was no coward. So when war came in 1914 he went to the front as an army chaplain and stretcher bearer.

Meanwhile the locum left in charge of St Martin's was an ambitious man, more than happy to serve the establishment status quo. He recognised that the eagle presented him with an opportunity. He had it displayed in the church, wrote and published a learned article on the subject and preached a rallying cry to the 'legions' needed, so the military leadership told everyone, to man the trenches across the channel.

It was from those same trenches that in due course Albion returned. Having been gassed and blown up he was mentally as well as physically scarred. As a result of his ordeal he had, and this was perhaps the hardest blow, become literally speechless, physically unable to give voice to the depths he held within him. The travesty that Saint Martin's had become in his absence was another crushing blow.

Having no choice but to suffer it in silence, he was able before the end, his diaries tell us to accept God's purpose even in that. However, Darke was among those lone few who at the time in the 1930s perceived the enormity of the threat that the rise of Hitler threatened. The figure of the eagle haunted him. The thought that this symbol might once again be the cause of unnecessary suffering and the loss of young lives drove him to a desperate act.

The nursing home where he was cared for by nuns was in his former parish. Whilst he attended services in the nuns' chapel, he could with great effort get to Saint Martin's. One Sunday evening, after the service was ended he was able to hide himself in the shadows so as deliberately to be locked in. Once alone in the church he took down the eagle from its place of prominence and throwing it on the floor broke it into pieces beyond the possibility of repair. It had been his discovery, but in his eyes had become the occasion of idolatry. Of course, he was discovered, as he knew he would be and offered no defence for his actions. On this occasion the church showed him mercy. He could have been charged with criminal damage. He could have been locked up in a mental hospital, but as the diaries which came to light after his death reveal he was perfectly sane. In the event a gentle and caring bishop arranged for him to continue to be cared for by the devoted nuns to the end of his days.'

'Darke's glory was hidden in brokenness' said Pilgrim, getting his breath back, his eyes wide with amazed compassion.' He reminds me of autumn buds around us. Their fragile beauty has been protected by the late autumn sun but they are destined never fully to open.'

'Albion Darke paid the prophet's price of not bowing down to the spirit of the age.' I replied 'He had the gift of universal vision that would not allow him to do such a thing.'

'As did the seer Saint John' said Pilgrim 'whose Gospel symbol, I perhaps need not tell you, is the eagle.'

'Other saints have seemed to have no fear when mud is slung at them.' I commented 'Now at last I think I understand why that is so.'

During the telling we had passed with what I now look back on as almost supernatural swiftness beyond Brightling and were now coming upon the town of our destination. Picturesque weather boarded buildings were interspersed among more modern frontages along a straggling main street, but I was looking for something to dominate the skyline and identify the physical centre of the settlement.

When I asked my friends where the church was they gave each other knowing looks and turned back to me with one of amused pity. 'We have enjoyed visiting and revisiting many good old Sussex parish churches and hearing the stories of faith they evoke, and many of them have stood witness for time out of mind' said Pilgrim 'but the gospel truth' he added with a wink 'is that although without a doubt there is a thriving community of Christians here, the last parish in Sussex has no ancient church building at its heart.'

'Just as the last book of the Bible, Saint John's Revelation tells us, there is no temple in the heavenly city.' said Who Knows. 'Beautiful though these human shrines are, the time will come when their purpose is served and they are no longer needed, just as at the end of our lives our physical nature is dispensed with.'

As the undoubted truth of what she was telling me sank in, I felt almost like shedding a tear, but turning back to the view of the town Who Knows summoned all her breath and saluted the sight with a determined cry 'Time to go!' and although with those words the full dawning of what must come next fully struck me it was above all the breathtaking sense of triumph that I was left with.

'Perhaps I shouldn't be saying this,' I began looking apologetically in Pilgrim's direction, but it's here, walking in the high woods that I feel Belloc's spirit nearer certainly than I did at his church when he was prayed for in a Latin requiem for all the undoubted beauty and spiritual depth of that service.'

'Don't apologise!' said Pilgrim 'If the service of the Mass is anything, then it is a service of dismissal, joyful sending out with heavenly manna for the journey.'

'HB felt himself at one with, the same substance as, the landscape.'

'The *muddy* landscape' added Who Knows.

'One substance, like the persons of the Trinity.' concluded Pilgrim ' Mud holds everything together – all you need is mud…!'

'Then,' I said 'I feel better about looking for the answers here!'

And now the solemn moment was ending with sad smiles. Robertsbridge remained an hour away I calculated, but I knew as Belloc had discovered that there was no point in clinging to that remaining time slipping away from me like the mud from under my feet as my fellow travellers turned to take their leave. Wondering if autumn in particular with its mists was their most suited season and environment I recalled the words of a great poet that 'In Heaven it is for ever autumn.' I had of course realised for some time that there was more to my companions than might at first have appeared. I saluted their sturdiness, their swiftness of eye, their courage and their humanity.

Over these days together my companions had revealed to me the very essence of Sussex; its rootedness, earthiness and spiritedness. The stories of good news always to be found in bad had been told, as if they had simply been waiting to be read from a holy landscape in which they are forever indelibly written and they had awoken in me a new sense of divine folly in the purposes of God. Yet there will be new stories of Sussex told and Sussex songs sung.

We walked on in deep silence and gradually I perceived a flickering in the substance of my friends. One moment Who Knows would be striding ahead the next she looked more like a tree walking. As Pilgrim faded in and out of view he seemed to take on the quality of bluish smoke as of incense rising than substance. Scribbler was becoming almost translucent except for the thin sketchy lines that remained making him much as one of his own cartoons.

So for the things these friends had bequeathed me I gave thanks as they turned and faded finally into the mist. Then I set off alone to walk the last part of the journey. I was enveloped in the fragrance of wood smoke with an almost ecclesiastical tang as of church incense about it, as if my friend Pilgrim was the last to leave me.

I realised my timeless pilgrimage had come to an end as I sank down in the seat of the train about to leave Robertsbridge and pulled out a mobile 'phone to leave a message that I was on my way home. Gazing idly out the carriage window I vaguely thought that the platform, thronged as it was with bustling passengers seemed un-usually busy for such a small rural station. Once or twice I even thought I recognised some of the faces, but they would turn the wrong way as if deliberately avoiding my scrutiny and I told myself I was tiredly over imaginative and mistaken. Then again, just at that point where the train begins to move away and you feel that momentary tug backwards I thought I glimpsed for a moment my erstwhile companions. I blinked hard and adjusted my spectacles cursing the condensation of my breath on the window and felt sure. But my attention was diverted by the steady enigmatic gaze of a fourth figure in their midst that seemed for half a second to directly meet mine, of a stout figure, who cut a sort of scruffy dignity with an old fashioned short black cape about his shoulders. Then as we picked up speed all became a blur. I found myself looking out at one Sussex scene superimposed in quick succession on another and feeling content in the knowledge that I was but a small part of the story, a song on the breeze that would never be lost.

Hilaire Belloc 1870 - 1953 was a prolific writer inspired by his deeply held Roman Catholic beliefs, his love of Sussex and a provocative sense of fun. The persona of this larger than life and clownish controversialist has become closely identified with his adopted home county and the imaginative account of his walk across Sussex with 'the Poet, Sailor and Grizzlebeard 'in 1902 was published ten years later in what has become a classic in the literature of the county **The Four Men**. Probably he is best remembered for his comic verse, still in print in **Cautionary Tales for Children**.

Taking **The Four Men** as his inspiration, rambling rector Nick Flint made his own walk in the 60th anniversary since Belloc's death. The titles of the chapters refer to the ancient names given to the four rivers which have both their mouths and their sources in Sussex. The Arun was known as Trisantonis, the Adur as Sore, the Ouse as Midwynd and the Cuckmere as Wandelmestrow.